The Science of Speed

The Art of the Sprint

The information in this book is meant to supplement, not replace, proper training. Like any sport involving speed, equipment, balance and environmental factors, running poses some inherent risk. The authors, editor and publisher advise readers to take full responsibility for their safety and know their limits. Before practicing the skills described in this book, be sure that your equipment and running surface is well maintained, and do not take risks beyond your level of experience, aptitude, training, and comfort level. Neither the authors nor the editor nor the publisher shall be held liable or responsible to any person or entity with respect to any loss or damages caused, or alleged to have been caused, directly or indirectly, by the information contained herein.

Please direct your inquiries to info@winningdimensions.com.

Dedication

In loving memory, I dedicate this book to my wife of 45 years, Kay Tellez.

Evelyn Lewis, mother to Carl and Carol Lewis, served as a source of inspiration to me. Her early coaching of these young, developing athletes focused on technique and improvement so that my work with them became a continuation of their training. I thank her for her support and guidance throughout my tenure.

I am also tremendously grateful to Roy and Mary Cullen for their friendship and their dedication to the Track and Field program at the University of Houston. They have been an ongoing source of motivation and encouragement to me and the UofH athletes on campus and throughout the United States for many years.

- Tom Tellez

Table of Contents

Acknowledgments

In addition to Evelyn Lewis, Coach Tellez would like to specifically thank the following coaches for the countless hours of practice, the desire to learn and the commitment to "getting it right" as he applied the science and refined his coaching system.

Dave Harewood has conducted research and has collaborated with Coach Tellez as he systematically applied the scientific principles of human motion to speed development.

Mike Takaha earned a BS in Kinesiology from UCLA. He served as Assistant Coach under Coach Tellez at the University of Houston for 20 years. .

Joe Douglas earned undergraduate degrees in Mathematics and Exercise Physiology from TCU and a master's degree in Mathematics from Oregon State. His PhD research at UCLA focused on exercise physiology and the effects of different training methods on athletes of similar talent. He is the Founder of the Santa Monica Track Club, which produced some of the world's greatest competitors and dozens of American, Olympic and world records.

Kyle Tellez earned a BS in Education from the University of Houston. He has entered his 26th season as an Assistant Coach at UH, focusing on the high jump, pole vault, javelin and multi events.

Steve Magness earned a BS in Kinesiology at the University of Houston and a MS in Exercise Science at George Mason University. He has coached for 13 years, currently serving as Head Cross-Country Coach at the University of Houston. He has also authored 3 books: <u>The Science of Running</u>, <u>Peak Performance</u> and <u>The Passion Paradox</u>.

Larry Silva earned a BA in Kinesiology from California State University Long Beach. He has been an Adjunct Professor and is currently the Head Track and Field Coach at Santa Monica College. He assisted Coach Tellez with the sprinters at the 2000 Olympic Trials and also coached for the Santa Monica Track Club.

Meme Garza earned a BA in Social Science at St. Edwards University and master's degree in Education from University of Texas – Brownsville. He served 42 years as Head Coach – Track and Cross Country for boys and girls at St. Joseph Academy.

Christopher J. Arellano, PhD, Biomechanics

Christopher J. Arellano is currently an Assistant Professor in the University of Houston's Health and Human Performance Department, with expertise in the biomechanics and energetics of human and animal locomotion. He earned a BS degree in Mechanical Engineering (with a concentration in Biomedical Engineering) at the University of Texas (UT) at Austin and went on to earn a Master of Science degree in Biomechanics and Motor Control at the University of Houston. These studies provided the foundation for him to be selected for the NASA Harriett G. Jenkins pre-doctoral fellowship, which provided the opportunity to earn his PhD in Integrative Physiology at the University of Colorado (CU) Boulder. At CU Boulder, he studied how humans maintain balance during walking and running and attempted to understand how different balance control strategies minimize metabolic cost. Shortly after, he completed a Postdoctoral fellowship at CU Boulder, studying how aging affects the ability to control movement. He then went on to work as a Postdoctoral Research Associate in the Department of Ecology and Evolutionary Biology at Brown University studying the significance of muscle-tendon shape change on locomotor movement. Dr. Arellano and his laboratory group at the University of Houston tackle problems that range from basic to applied, but the topic of human running and sprinting remains an integral part of his scientific curiosity and interest.

Dr. Arellano's contribution to this book was to write Chapter 1 – The Physics of Human Motion. He also provided extensive expertise and oversight to underscore the scientific principles underlying the coaching details included in Chapters 2 and 3.

Kerry B. Sprick, Editor

Kerry B. Sprick is a visionary educator and performance coach with extensive background in business operations and leadership. She completed her undergraduate education at the University of Chicago with a degree in Behavioral Science. After a 28-year sales and management career in the Fortune 500 technology sector, she established a consultancy that helps small business owners and individuals accomplish their most challenging goals. With a focus on the psychology of habit formation and change, Ms. Sprick utilizes systematic techniques to confirm motivation, uncover real and perceived obstacles and manage commitment to lead her clients to success. Ms. Sprick met Carl Lewis in 2015 and discovered a shared passion for helping individuals achieve their maximum potential. Together they launched The Perfect Method® project, which highlights the physical preparation, mastery of technical skills and mental discipline required for athletic success. The project paired Ms. Sprick's business acumen and psychology skills with the factors that led to Mr. Lewis' unparalleled competitive achievement, including the technical skills taught to him by Coach Tom Tellez. They added a Success Template to instill the habits required for individual success - both on and off the track. They developed an online curriculum, presented at dozens of symposiums and clinics, and partnered with the Amateur Athletic Union with a vision to positively affect the coaching community and the next generation of youth athletes.

With this book, Ms. Sprick now presents the knowledge, technical prescriptions and teaching experience of Coach Tellez in a way that expands its value to the athletic community and preserves it for future generations of coaches and athletes.

Elissa Sorojsrisom, Illustrator

Ms. Sorojsrisom is a scientific researcher and natural science illustrator. She earned her ScB in Biology from Brown University and also holds a certificate in Natural Science Illustration from Rhode Island School of Design. She has studied bat flight biomechanics, bat wing morphology, the evolution of CAM photosynthesis, and leaf shape development. She has illustrated subjects as varied as the anatomy of the human nervous system, fossil horseshoe crabs, stinging tentilla of siphonophores, bat wing microstructure, a new species of Australian redmaid, and extinct sea cucumbers. Her work has been featured in publications including *Sports Medicine, Royal Society, Scientific Reports, Geological Magazine, Frontiers in Neuroanatomy,* and *Systematic Biology.*

About the Cover

"Sprinter" was created by Edith Peres-Lethmate (1927-2017) in celebration of the 1984 Olympic Games. Edith Peres-Lethmate was a German sculptor who began in woodworking, then learned to work with clay, glass and metal. She practiced sports for many years and is best known for her sports sculptures. Exhibitions of her work have been held in Frankfurt, Cologne, Berlin, Basel, Dijon, Los Angeles and San Francisco.

We are grateful to the family of Ms. Peres-Lethmate for the permission to include an image of her work on the cover of this book. A large-scale version called "Sprinter at the Koret" sits at the entry of the University of San Francisco's Koret Health and Recreation Center in San Francisco, California

Foreword

The best way I can describe Tom Tellez as a coach is to share a scene from the summer of 1984. We were in Los Angeles for my first Olympics. After years of training and competing as a sprinter and long jumper, I had just won my first Olympic gold medal – in the 100 meters – and I could not have been happier.

On the way out of the stadium, I saw Coach Tellez, who I figured would be just as excited as I was. Eager to hear his reaction to the race, I asked him what he thought. His first words were: "Technically, you were bad out of the blocks. You should have broken the world record."

It was vintage Coach Tellez: straight to the point and laser-focused on technique. I had never met a coach who knew more about the technical aspects of track and field – the science of our sport – than the man we call Coach T.

All these years later, that memory from the 1984 Games still makes me smile. It also reminds me how Coach T always locked in on the smallest of details – the angle of every body part, every force being exerted – in order to yield big results.

He started coaching in Germany while serving in the army during the late 1950s. In the late 1970s, after coaching at several high schools and junior colleges in California, Coach T became head coach at the University of Houston – a move that ended up being great not only for him, but also for me and for so many other athletes as well.

In 1979, I joined him as a Houston Cougar. It was a big move for a kid from New Jersey. But I sure was fortunate that Coach T took me in, and we worked together throughout my entire professional career. Technically, Coach Tellez was light-years ahead of all the other coaches I ever came across. He was always about the science. Every workout was high quality and effective, but we also had a lot of fun.

Everything I ever accomplished in track and field – breaking world records and winning nine Olympic gold medals ending with the long jump at the 1996 Games – I never could have done any of it without Coach T. That's why I'm so pleased that he is now sharing what he knows – his vast array of priceless knowledge – in book form.

Coaches and athletes alike will benefit from what Coach T offers here. And his book comes at a perfect time. Now that I've joined the coaching ranks – also at the University of Houston – I have seen way too much bad information being put out by all levels of coaches across the country. Young track-and-field athletes of today do not need gimmicks and fads. They need to learn the true science of our sport. Simply put, both the coaches and athletes of today could have no better teacher than Tom Tellez.

Introduction

IF YOU WANT YOUR ATHLETE TO RUN THEIR FASTEST,
THEY HAVE TO RUN WITH THE CORRECT TECHNIQUE.
WHAT'S CORRECT HAS TO BE BASED ON SCIENCE."

- TOM TELLEZ

Speed applies to every competitive sport. If you want to run your fastest, you must run with the correct technique.

Coaches and parents, you are the teachers. You teach what you know, your knowledge comes from personal experience and, thankfully, you continue to pursue knowledge. In your quest for knowledge, you speak with colleagues, attend seminars, read books and perhaps study YouTube videos of world-class athletes. Like the athletes you are training, you are constantly searching for the answers that will deliver the desired result. You seek the best prescription to follow.

The challenge is that sometimes you find incomplete or perhaps overly complicated answers. Or, the information you gather may be wrong. This is not OK. What you teach should always be grounded in solid science.

When it comes to the technical skills required for speed, the principles of physics and kinesiology – the engineering of the human body - must be used as the foundation for human motion. These principles have been the same for many many years, and their correct application has produced some of the fastest athletes in history.

That is why we can say *there is only one way to run your fastest*. Because there is only one way, we know any coach can teach it. And any athlete can learn it.

The challenge is in explaining the science in a way that's understandable – and then applying it correctly – so anyone can coach, learn and correctly execute what it takes to produce maximum speed. From there, *wisdom gained from the experience of those who have produced the fastest athletes* adds invaluable insight, tools and coaching recommendations that will quickly correct commonly observed problems and behaviors.

These are the elements of a coaching system that will work every time – and help every athlete achieve their potential.

For the very first time, this book presents the work of **Tom Tellez.** Raised in California, he attended Montebello High School and Fullerton College. He obtained a B.A. in Biology and Physical Education from Whittier College and a master's degree in Education at Chapman College. His master's thesis was on the mechanical analysis of the shotput using cinematography.

Tom Tellez began his coaching career at Buena Park High School, then went on to coach at Fullerton College and UCLA. He moved to Houston and served twenty-two seasons as the Head Track & Field Coach at the University of Houston and the Santa Monica Track Club. From 1984-96, six of the seven U.S. sprinters who won Olympic Gold medals were coached by Tom Tellez and seven of the USA's thirteen overall medals were claimed by his athletes.

Coach Tellez is a member of the U.S. Track Coaches Association Hall of Fame. His achievements led to several international coaching appointments, including Head Coach for the 1991 U.S. World Championships team, Head Coach for the 1987 Pan American team, and assistant coach for the 1980 and 1984 U.S.A. Olympic Teams.

Tom Tellez developed some of the greatest track and field performers in the history of the sport, including:

Carl Lewis (5-time Olympian, 9 Olympic Gold medals, 1 Olympic Silver medal, 8 World Championships, former 100m WR holder, current WR holder - Long Jump Indoors and multiple NCAA titles)
Joe DeLoach (NCAA and Olympic 200m Gold medalist)
Leroy Burrell (Olympic Gold medalist, former 100m WR holder, 3-time NCAA champion)
Kirk Baptiste (Olympic 200m Silver medalist)
Mike Marsh (Olympic 200m Gold medalist)
Floyd Heard (200m Olympian and American Record holder)
Mark Witherspoon (100m Olympian)
Sam Jefferson (100m NCAA Champion)
Stanley Floyd (100m sprinter favored for Olympics, but denied due to U.S. boycott)
Darius Pemberton (Indoor National Champion, 55m Hurdles)

Carol Lewis (3-time Olympian, 4-time U.S. Champion, 4-time NCAA Champion, Long Jump)
Michelle Finn Burrell (Olympic 4x100 Gold medalist, Olympic 200m finalist, Olympic Trials 200m Bronze medalist, 3-time U.S. and NCAA Indoors 60m Champion (2x while at FSU), U.S. and NCAA Outdoors 100m Champion while at FSU)
Jackie Washington (Olympian and 3-time All-American sprinter)
Patsy Walker (AIAW National Champion, Heptathlon and Pentathlon)
Jenny Adams (Indoor and Outdoor National Champion, Long Jump)
Jolanda Jones (3-time NCAA Champion, Heptathlon)

Coach Tellez studied and applied physics and kinesiology to break down all aspects of running mechanics so he could convert that knowledge into a prescription to produce speed. He conducted research, analyzed film and applied proven scientific principles to running and sprint technique. From there, he developed a model to use as the basis for coaching all track and field events.

Coach Tellez' application of science to speed development, along with his coaching methodology, is scientifically sound and timeless. His system and coaching techniques continue to produce consistent results. His assistance is still sought, decades after he first began coaching.

This book is the culmination of interviews, lab research, review of papers, lectures and seminars, hands-on athletic training and video footage analysis. We have assessed the world's fastest athletes and transferred the specifics into easy-to-understand illustrations.[1] Tips for coaches and quotes from Tom Tellez are also included.

Our objective is to provide the scientific foundation and link the science to running mechanics in a way that every athlete, coach and parent can understand. We break down all the details for maximum speed, because EVERY DETAIL MATTERS.

How to Use the Book

Athletes, coaches and parents, this book is a resource to explain and apply the science to help every athlete produce their best results. Use it as a reference guide.

In this book, you will learn:

- The laws of human motion and the science of correct running technique
- How correct technique optimizes application of force on the ground and generates speed
- The very specific elements to study and train for sprints and distance running
- How to identify and correct problems
- A consistent vocabulary to use in teaching what to do and why
- How to change motor patterns for consistent results
- For coaches, the best cues to give your athletes for success

---

[1] A reference list is included to highlight some of the classic and more recent work on running and sprinting mechanics. This list is not intended to be exhaustive.

The flow of the book is to start with the "why" and gradually move to the "what" and "how". We move from the complicated and abstract in Chapter 1 to the simple and actionable details in Chapters 2 through 5.

Using the Vocabulary list in APPENDIX A as needed, we suggest that you read Chapters 1 and 2 while referring to the *un-edited video frames of a youth sprinter* in APPENDICES C and D. This 13-year-old athlete shows the correct running and start mechanics in action, and we have marked the images and noted the elements. Then read the remaining chapters to learn how to apply the principles to sprinting and distance running.

Refer back to the book often. Always connect the technique with the science. Stay grounded in the principles, focus on every detail, and strive for consistent, correct execution.

COACHES NOTE

If you have any questions or comments about the material we have presented, please write to us at info@winningdimensions.com.

The information in this book is applicable for all athletes, regardless of age or gender and can be applied to ANY SPORT that requires speed. That said, we must establish the premise that *not every athlete will be fast, but every athlete can get faster.*

Chapter 1

The Physics of Human Motion

FOR ANY MOVEMENT TO OCCUR, THE LEVER MUST ROTATE AROUND ITS AXIS. THE ORIGIN OF MOVEMENT IS ROTARY."

- TOM TELLEZ

Running and sprint speed is a result of *correct* application of force to the ground in a specific amount of time. For an athlete to attain and maintain maximum speed, the magnitude of this force must be extremely high and oriented in the right direction. The production and utilization of force must be optimal and efficient.

There are three building blocks to understand:

1. The physics of motion, as applied to humans
2. The biomechanical principles that underlie the ability of an athlete to generate force and momentum
3. How to apply these principles to each stage of a run to develop, maximize and sustain speed while minimizing risk of injury.

The Fundamental Principles

Newton's Three Laws of Motion

The fundamental principles were established by Newton:

1. A body at rest will stay at rest and a body in motion will stay in motion unless acted upon by an unbalanced force.
2. The acceleration of an object is dependent upon the net force acting upon the object and the mass of the object.
3. For every action, there is an equal and opposite reaction.

Formulas that Apply Newton's Laws of Motion to Speed

Textbook formulas allow us to apply the laws of motion specifically to running and the development and maintenance of speed.

1. Velocity   = Δ position/ time
2. Acceleration   = Δ velocity / Δ time
3. Force   = mass x acceleration

4.	Impulse	= force x time
5.	Momentum	= mass x Δ velocity
6.	Work	= force x Δ position
7.	Power	= force x velocity
		= force x (Δ position/time)
		= Work / time
8.	Load	= mass x gravity
9.	Moment arm	= distance of load from axis of rotation
10.	Torque	= force x moment arm

Let's establish how these formulas relate to each other and how they apply to running and sprinting.

1. **Velocity**: Because velocity is a vector quantity, it has magnitude and direction. Velocity is "change in position" in a given direction over time. In coaching, we often use the term "speed" to mean the same thing; however, speed is a scalar quantity and reflects magnitude without direction. In this book, we focus on "velocity" but sometimes use "speed" and "velocity" interchangeably in the text in ways that are familiar to coaches and athletes.

2. **Acceleration and Force:** We refer to Newton's 2nd law of motion to understand the relation between force and acceleration during running and sprinting.

$$Force = mass \ x \ acceleration$$

Newton's second law tells us there is a cause and effect relation between force and acceleration, assuming the athlete's body mass remains constant. This means that if unbalanced forces are applied to the body, the effect is a change in the body's acceleration. So, to increase the body's acceleration, the athlete must apply a force that will move their body. The way to *achieve this is by pushing against the ground.*

3. **Action and Reaction Force**: Newton's 3rd Law states that for every action force, there is an equal and opposite reaction force. A simple example is when a person is standing on the ground with the body upright. There are two external forces acting on the body, one being the force due to gravity (mass x gravity), which is equal to body weight. What is important to understand is

22

that a person's body weight is applying a force to the ground and in turn, the ground reacts with an equal and opposite force that is applied to the body. This is the second external force, which is known as the ground reaction force. As long as those two forces remain equal and opposite, a person will remain standing upright. In the context of motion, Newton's 3rd Law is the basis for why we can run. It is only because we can apply a force to the ground by pushing on the ground as hard we can. The force we create with our leg is pushing down and back. In turn, the ground reacts with a force that is equal and opposite; therefore, the ground pushes the body up and forward, enabling the athlete to change and increase their forward momentum.

4. **Impulse-Momentum** and **Work-Energy** frameworks: Because the basis for this book is founded on Newton's laws of motion, it is helpful and useful to understand the causes that underlie maximum speed in the context of these principles.

   A. Impulse-Momentum Framework:

   A simple explanation for how impulse and momentum apply to running and sprinting is that the impulse-momentum theorem stems from Newton's 2nd law of motion

   $$F = m\mathbf{a}$$

   and can be shown by first expressing acceleration as a Δ *velocity* /Δ *time*:

   $$F = m \times (\Delta\ velocity\ /\ \Delta\ time)$$

   We can now re-arrange and bring Δ *time* to the left side as follows

   $$F \times \Delta\ time = m \times \Delta\ velocity$$

   The left-hand side is known as the "impulse" caused by a net force F applied to the body during an interval of time. The most important point to understand is that the net force F must be large enough to move the body, i.e. to produce a change in the body's momentum.

Deriving the impulse-momentum theorem allows us to understand the primary determinants that will change the body's momentum, i.e., going from zero velocity to maximum velocity.

How does the athlete apply an impulse to the body so that the impulse results in a change in their body's momentum? The impulse-momentum theorem tells us that the athlete must apply force to the ground. More specifically, the force that is generated along the ground must be large enough to overcome the force due to gravity and force due to friction and air resistance so that the athlete can move the body in the up and down *and* forward direction. *Further, in order to increase the impulse applied to the ground, the athlete must either increase force and/or the time of its application.*

"Impulse" is a less common term than "power" in the running and sprinting world. Those familiar with the concept of power and who use this term are approaching their understanding using a Work-Energy framework.

B.   Work-Energy Framework:

The work done by the net force F applied to the body equals to a change in the kinetic energy of the body, expressed as

$$\text{Force·displacement} = W_{tot} = K_{final} - K_{initial} = \tfrac{1}{2}\, mv_{final}^2 - \tfrac{1}{2}\, mv_{initial}^2$$

In the context of a race, you can see that difference between the final and initial kinetic energy is the *change* in kinetic energy. During running and sprinting, the athlete does work on the body because the body undergoes a displacement in the up and down *and* forward direction as force is applied to the ground.

The equation above is used as a general way to think about how an athlete produces a net force F while the body undergoes a displacement, measured from the initial starting line to the finish line.

When thinking about the concept of power, we must consider how much time it takes to get the work done. Power is defined as the total work performed over time. As such, coaches and trainers often use the term "power" when characterizing an athlete who is faster than another. As an example, compare two athletes with the same mass (body weight), where one athlete sprints a 100-meter distance in 9.95 seconds and the other who sprints the same distance in 10.15 seconds. By definition, the sprinter with the faster time has the capacity to generate more power; i.e., they can do the same amount of work to move their body down the track in less time. This is true, and much emphasis is placed on the ability of an athlete to generate more power. However, *it is possible that two athletes can generate the same amount of total power, but the one who applies maximum force in the correct direction will be faster.*

Our intention in this book is to focus on correct technique and to coach every athlete correctly. Therefore, we strive to understand and communicate how force is generated and optimized during each stride during each phase of a run – within the biological limits of generating that force.

Both frameworks rely on the fundamental idea that an athlete must apply force to the ground and that the force must be large enough to move the body down the track. Regardless of whether we use the term "impulse" or "power", our attention is focused on the magnitude AND direction of force, all in the context of how to achieve maximum velocity. By the end of this book, we hope you will appreciate the fundamental importance of correct application of force, how that is the underlying factor in determining maximum velocity, and most importantly, how to coach it correctly.

5. **Momentum** is a vector, and there are two kinds of momentum - angular (circular) and linear. We will refer to both kinds in this book.

6. Every joint involved in an exercise has a **moment arm**: one is from the muscle and the other from the load. The muscle moment arm is defined by the perpendicular distance of the muscle's force from the axis of rotation. The load moment arm is defined by the perpendicular distance of the load from the axis of rotation **(Fig.1)**. If muscle force, muscle moment arm and the load are held constant, a shorter load moment arm will require less torque to move the limb. Otherwise, a longer load moment arm will require more torque to move the limb.

The leg and arm can change their load moment arms because we can re-configure the limb (through flexion and extension) to change the distance of the limb's Center of Mass (COM) relative to its axis of rotation. *Overall, an athlete benefits from reconfiguring their legs and arms, especially when they need to rapidly swing the limbs.* This is especially important for the sprinter.

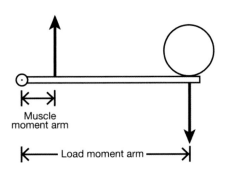

Figure 1 – The Moment Arm.

7. The **Center of Mass (COM)** of the body is where the physical location of the body's entire mass is concentrated and where gravity acts on the body. In the context of physics, we use this reference point to understand how the COM moves in the up and down and forward direction during running and sprinting.

    It's also important to understand that each segment of the body has its own COM, located some distance away from its joint axis of rotation. Overall, the COM position of the body and body segments will change during running and sprinting. *Understanding the behavior of the COM is fundamental to understanding running and sprinting mechanics.*

How We Create Motion in the Human Body

Lever Systems

The human body is like a machine, better yet, a biological machine. It's built with a series of muscle-driven lever systems that enable it to move. In humans, our bones, ligaments and tendons act as integral parts of the lever systems. Our joints are axes of rotation, and our muscles act as force generators.

Lever systems come in several varieties and are identified by the way the individual lever is arranged around its axis and how opposing forces act upon it.

A **Class 1 lever system** looks like a seesaw, where the opposing forces of load vs. effort are balanced around the axis. In the human body, the area where the skull meets the top of the spine is a good example of a Class 1 lever system **(Fig. 2)**.

Take a moment and practice this concept: Lift your chin all the way up, drop it forward and repeat the motion.

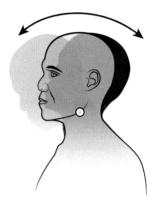

**Figure 2 – The head as an example
of a Class 1 Lever System.**

That's a Class 1, balanced lever system.

As a secondary point, take notice of how the surrounding muscles stretch and contract to support the movement.

 The lever system that enables the running motion is a **Class 3 system**, *where the effort is closer to the axis than the load.*

A good example of a human Class 3 lever system in use is bending the arm: The axis is at the elbow, and the weight of the forearm acts as the resistance.

The *biceps* muscle produces force while shortening, eliciting elbow flexion. The forearm rotates upward and lifts the load created by the weight of the forearm and hand. The bicep is closer to the elbow than the forearm and hand (**Fig. 3**).

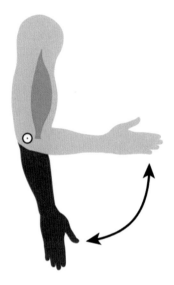

Figure 3 – The arm as an example of a Class 3 Lever System.

There are additional Class 3 lever systems that affect the running motion. The two dominant systems are:

- In the leg, with the axis of rotation at the knee. The *hamstring* muscle provides the effort to lift the lower leg upward.

- In the hip, where the *flexors* lift the femur upward as it overcomes the entire weight of the leg.

There are trade-offs when changing the configuration of the limbs, as this may change the muscle force demands to move the limbs. We will review these trade-offs as we apply these principles to our understanding of how we create motion and speed.

Types of Motion Within the Body and in Relation to the Ground

Motion within the body is created by forces that are acting on the lever systems.

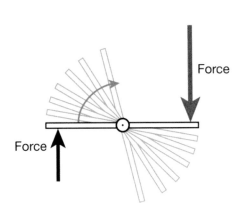

Figure 4 – Unequal torques cause motion around the axis of rotation.

For any movement to occur, a lever must rotate around its axis. **Rotary motion** is created when the forces from muscles produce opposing, rotating torques about the joints in clockwise and counterclockwise directions **(Fig.4)**.

If torques are equal, the lever won't rotate. If they're unequal, the lever will rotate around the axis in the direction of the greater torque.

Here, torque is created by the application of a linear force from the muscles acting about the joint's moment arm.

Linear motion is movement that occurs in a straight line **(Fig. 5)**.

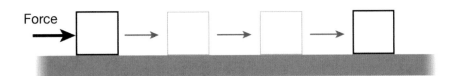

Figure 5 – Linear motion occurs in a straight line.

Variables such as mass, distance, velocity and acceleration come into play in the discussion of linear motion.

Translatory motion occurs when all points in a mass move the same distance in the same amount of time, but may not be moving in a straight line.

How We Generate Linear Velocity

The most efficient runner *directs and concentrates available forces* that allow them to push on the ground and move the body in a forward direction. Because the resulting force on the ground has both a horizontal and vertical component, this is how an athlete overcomes inertia and gravity - to generate forward motion or linear velocity.

The whole body, along with its individual lever systems, are all working together and undergoing some form of rotary and linear motion to increase the body's linear velocity. *Maximum linear velocity is the result of optimal hip rotation and leg turnover, but the underlying objective throughout any run is to continue to correctly apply force to the ground.*

Let's break this process down. Newton's 2nd and 3rd Laws of Motion are involved in the following manner:

First, the formula

$$F = ma$$

where   force (cause) = body mass x acceleration (effect)

To overcome the force due to gravity acting on the body, an athlete must generate a downward force on the ground that is greater than their body weight. To overcome the body's inertia, friction, and air resistance that all resist forward motion, the athlete must also generate a backward force on the ground.

Then, the key is to *direct the ground force* to move the body upward <u>*and*</u> forward.

As an example, any athlete who runs, whether sprinting or running a marathon, must overcome inertia and gravity at the start. *With or without blocks*, force must be applied to the ground through the legs and directed toward the body's COM at the optimal angle **(Fig. 6)**.

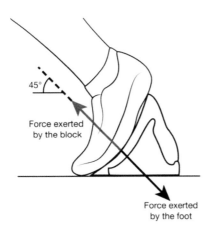

Force exerted
by the block

Force exerted
by the foot

**Figure 6 – Forces exerted
at the block start.**

Then, as the athlete accelerates, force must continue to be applied in the correct direction in the least amount of time to overcome gravity and build momentum.

These details are especially important for short distance sprinters because they must maximize magnitude and direction in EVERY stride. Also, there are significant transitions in body position and arm stroke to manage in very little time – from start to finish.

COACHES NOTE

The correct application of force specifically affects:

- The mechanics of the start when forces must overcome inertia and gravity
- The athlete's ability to accelerate to attain maximum speed
- The athlete's time of deceleration

Whether running for recreation or professional competition, the athlete with the greatest increase in momentum and hence linear velocity will slow down for the least amount of time…and that's how races are won.

How Rearranging the Lever Contributes to Speed

There are three variables at play here: 1) the lever system's moment arm that determines the muscle-induced torque; 2) the lever's speed of rotation, and 3) the lever system's range of motion. For the lever system to help produce maximum speed, it must move through its full range of motion as quickly as possible.

Assuming a Class 3 lever system where the muscle force is closer to the axis of rotation than the load, rearranging the lever will influence the muscular effort needed to move the lever AND affect its speed of rotation. *There are trade-offs to optimize in a Class 3 lever system, and these are especially important for sprinters.*

Let's use the example of two swinging pendulums with different lengths.

Their range of motion (also called their **angular displacement**) is the same, but the **linear displacement** is greater for the pendulum with the longer length **(Fig. 7)**.

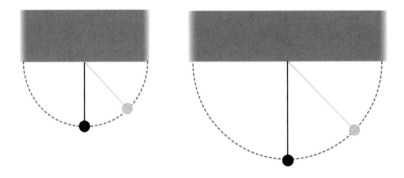

Figure 7 – The pendulum with the longer length will experience a greater linear displacement, even though the pendulums undergo the same range of motion.

To demonstrate this concept, swing a fully extended arm in the forward and backward direction (like a pendulum). With the arm extended, we can think of this scenario as increasing the arm's pendulum length. The pendulum length is the distance from the shoulder's axis of rotation to a point on the arm that would have the same **moment of inertia** as if the entire arm's mass were concentrated at that point. Simply put, when we increase the pendulum length by extending the elbow, the pendulum (the arm) undergoes a greater displacement when compared to an arm that is bent at the elbow.

However, a pendulum with a longer length is also harder to swing. Lengthening the pendulum increases the distance of the load from the axis of rotation, requiring a greater amount of muscle force and torque to either maintain the position of the pendulum or to move the pendulum at the same angular velocity.

While a higher muscle force and torque is needed to rotate a longer pendulum at the same angular velocity as a shorter one, *a longer pendulum will generate a higher centripetal acceleration.* **Centripetal acceleration** is what keeps an object in circular motion and is directed toward the center of the circle.

A higher centripetal acceleration generates a higher centripetal force that can be applied by the arm which, in sprinting, can translate to a force that is applied to the ground.

Let's break this down by using the arm as an example:

We can imagine the arm as moving along a circular path where an acceleration component is acting along the centripetal direction, i.e., toward the shoulder's axis of rotation. We can use the formula for centripetal acceleration as:

$$a_c = \omega^2 r$$

where ω equals the angular velocity and r is the arm's pendulum length.

Let's assume that the angular velocity remains the same during the downward swing of the arm stroke regardless of whether the arm is bent or extended. This tells us that a higher centripetal acceleration can be generated by simply increasing r, which can be achieved by extending the elbow.

On the other hand, let's review what happens when the pendulum length is decreased. If we assume that a muscle-induced torque generates the same angular velocity of the swinging arm, then a shorter pendulum will decrease r and thus, decrease the centripetal acceleration generated by the swinging arm.

How does changing the arm's pendulum length affect running speed?

By extending the elbow during the downward motion of the arm stroke, the athlete effectively increases its pendulum length and hence, its centripetal acceleration. The consequence is *an increase in the force that is applied to the ground during landing and takeoff on the opposite side* **(Fig. 8a)**.

Figure 8a – Opening the elbow on the downstroke increases application of force to the ground on the opposite side.

Conversely, by flexing the elbow during the upstroke, the athlete is shortening its pendulum length and helping to increase its speed of rotation **(Fig. 8b)**.

Closing the elbow makes it easier to bring the arm forward at the same or faster velocity to prepare the arm for the next downward stroke.

Figure 8b – Closing the elbow on the upstroke increases its speed of rotation.

Now let's examine how changing pendulum length in the leg affects the stride cycle.

Regarding leg swing, the hip is the axis of rotation for the leg, while the knee joint acts to shorten or lengthen the pendulum (in this case the shank and the foot) when necessary. When completing the recovery of the swinging leg, flexion at the knee reconfigures the leg to shorten its pendulum length and help rotate it faster with less muscular effort.

At landing and takeoff, the foot-ground contact point is the axis of rotation for the body's COM. When the athlete extends the leg at the hip and correctly applies force to the ground, the body's COM moves forward and covers maximum ground. Then, as the knee flexes during flight, *the pendulum shortens which increases its speed* of rotation to prepare for the next landing **(Fig. 9)**.

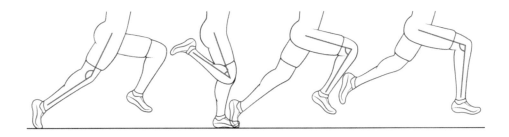

Figure 9 – Changes in the leg's pendulum length are due to knee flexion and extension.

As we will see in Chapter 2, the combination of optimal hip rotation, knee extension and flexion with proper foot placement allows the athlete to apply maximum force to the ground, in the correct direction and in the least amount of time.

These elements enable the athlete to accelerate from the ground faster and travel farther.

Mechanisms that Facilitate Rapid Swinging of the Limbs and Contribute to Speed

Optimal extension and flexion of lever systems involve additional actions that enhance the force output of muscle-tendon systems. The first is the **stretch-shortening cycle** of muscle, where active muscle lengthens before shortening, allowing for greater force production. There is also the possibility that, during this preceding stretch, energy is temporarily stored in elastic elements such as tendons, which are structures that behave in series and in parallel to the muscle. So, the stretch-shortening cycle of muscle-tendon units likely involves stretch of muscle fibers and/or elastic elements, both of which will help increase the amount of force that drives limb movement.

Another action called the **stretch reflex** is an involuntary muscle contraction, which facilitates the return of an excessively stretched muscle to its original state. Controlled by the central nervous system, the stretch reflex is intended to protect the muscle and its connective tissue so they can respond properly to voluntary movement patterns.

An example of these **force-enhancing mechanisms** in action occurs during the athlete's downward arm stroke. At the last phase of the downward swing, the athlete pulls the elbow back to almost a full 90-degree angle to stretch the shoulder muscle-tendon systems that includes the anterior deltoid and pectoralis major. During the upstroke, the system responds with an elastic "spring-like" action that increases the angular velocity of the entire arm **(Fig. 10)**.

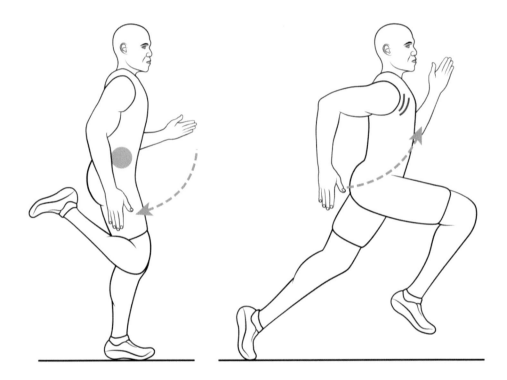

Figure 10 – Changes in both pendulum length and force-enhancing mechanisms during the arm stroke help to achieve maximum speed.

Another example is the part of the stride cycle when the foot is in contact with the ground. Between landing and takeoff, the athlete applies force to the ground by pushing down and back. As this occurs the hip extends, initiating a stretch of the hip flexor muscle-tendon system which includes the rectus femoris. This stretch also initiates the stretch reflex mechanism. Together, they increase the angular velocity of the leg so it will fold up (by way of reconfiguring the leg by knee flexion) and rapidly swing forward in preparation for the next landing phase **(Fig. 11)**.

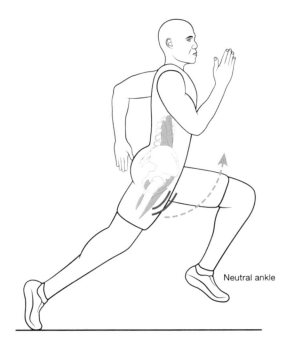

Neutral ankle

Figure 11 – Force-enhancing mechanisms at the hip also increase angular velocity of the leg as it swings through.

When performed correctly, the muscles and elastic tissue elements act like a rubber band, when stretched and then let go.

The force-enhancing mechanisms that arise during a stretch that precedes shortening can be felt at the shoulder and in the hip when sprinting. *These mechanisms will help elicit a greater force to accelerate the arms and legs, which is crucial to achieve and sustain maximum speed.* We will continually apply the concept of these force-enhancing mechanisms as key factors that the athlete should exploit to rapidly apply force and swing the limbs.

The Athlete's Center of Mass

The **Center of Mass (COM)** position is the balance point of an object in relation to the application of force. COM position is an important factor that affects linear velocity. In humans, the body's COM is the point around which the body is most free to move and, on the average person, is usually just above the navel.

The location of the COM in relation to application of force is essential to correct running mechanics beginning at the start and with every stride **(Fig. 12)**.

Figure 12 – The approximate location of the COM in the blocks and during the stride. Ideally, reaction forces are directed toward the COM.

Ideally, the athlete wants to position their body so that the reaction force applied from the block is oriented toward the whole-body COM, pushing up and forward to maximize COM acceleration in the forward direction. As the athlete reaches maximum speed, the ground force gradually shifts toward pushing more in the upward direction than in the forward direction.

Note also that every individual body segment also has a COM. The COM is discussed in more detail in the next chapters, as we break down the correct mechanics of the start and stride cycle.

Summary

In this chapter, we reviewed the physical principles that form the foundation for human motion. Applying these principles helps us understand how to create motion and develop speed. There is much commonality within the formulas: forces, mass, velocity, time. We must pay attention to how an athlete can best apply these principles to generate the forces required to increase velocity and then how to minimize the forces that will also be acting to slow the athlete down.

The clever optimization of the body's lever systems will either generate force or increase the velocity of the limbs. Understanding and executing these elements, along with correct application of force to the body's COM, are key to proper running mechanics and achieving maximum speed.

The objective is to make sure the forces and mechanics of motion are optimized.

By understanding how parts of the body work together to move, and how the athlete can apply force at the right time to build momentum, we can develop the best possible training regimens and help every athlete run their fastest.

Note that while these principles apply to all runners – marathoners and sprinters alike - *each* athlete will have their own set of optimal parameters. These optimal parameters are what the coach and athlete must learn.

Chapter 2

Applying Physics for Correct Running

and Sprinting Technique

SPEED ISN'T ABOUT QUICKNESS. IT'S A FUNCTION OF HOW MUCH FORCE IS APPLIED TO THE GROUND OVER A GIVEN AMOUNT OF TIME.

THE ATHLETE NEEDS TO FOCUS ON THE APPLICATION OF FORCE, NOT STRIDE FREQUENCY. STRIDE FREQUENCY IS USELESS IN THE ABSENCE OF FORCE."

- TOM TELLEZ

The scientific principles that drive human motion and the increase in linear velocity explained earlier will now be applied directly to running technique.

Many athletes and coaches emphasize stride frequency and quickness as they work on technique; however, stride frequency in and of itself does not cause motion. The application of force in the correct direction is required.

As depicted in Appendix B, the correct application of force – the forces exerted and the time forces act - is what is required to generate optimal stride frequency, stride length and ultimately speed. The mechanical importance of correct body position, arm stroke and the variables that affect stride length are explained in this chapter. When applied correctly as individual elements of a complete system, these aspects combine to generate the strongest horizontal and vertical forces that allow an athlete to achieve maximum speed.

Body Position Determines How Far the Body Will Travel with Each Stride

Body position is the most important factor in running and sprinting technique. Body position here is defined as the orientation of the hips and how the torso and hips are aligned in relation to the lower body segments during various moments within the stride cycle. Specific mechanics create spatial and temporal characteristics of the stride which serve to maximize or inhibit the application of force.

From Chapter 1, we know that *optimal hip rotation and leg turnover are crucial to increasing and maintaining speed.*

From landing through takeoff, body position determines the location of the athlete's COM and determines the path and position of the hips and legs. Consequently, body position is responsible for the timing between when the foot makes contact with the ground and then leaves the ground.

Let's review three scenarios based on COM location.

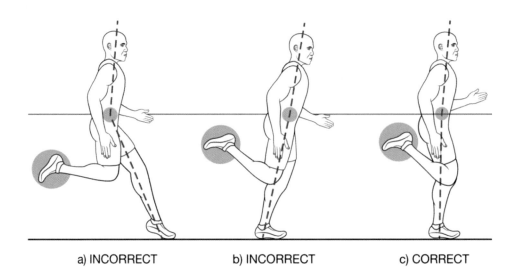

a) INCORRECT   b) INCORRECT   c) CORRECT

Figure 13 (a,b,c) – The COM location and body angle in relation to the landing leg determines landing distance, takeoff distance and stride length.

COM Behind the Landing Leg - INCORRECT TECHNIQUE

The pelvis is tilted forward, so the *COM is positioned behind the landing leg* in **Figure 13(a)**. Visually, the landing foot is ahead of the knee, which causes a pulling or "pawing" action against the ground. This body position presents several negative consequences to speed development:

1. Hip rotation slows down because the athlete must wait longer for the COM to travel over the leg.

2. The athlete is likely to produce unnecessary braking forces that will result in a loss of momentum. The athlete will stay longer on the ground and less force will be applied in the correct direction. It is true that if the leg swings backward fast enough, the leg can generate a propulsive force, which may help momentarily to accelerate the body forward. This *propulsive force, however, will be followed by an unnecessarily greater braking force* because the ground force will push UPWARD and BACKWARD on the athlete, rather than directly UPWARD toward the COM.

Figure 14 highlights the effects of this body position on landing and takeoff distance, as compared with the correct body position.

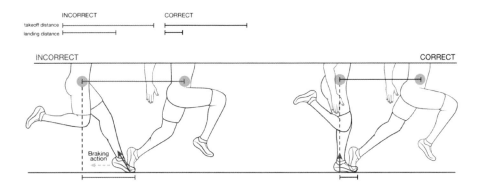

Figure 14 – When compared to the correct body position, if the COM is behind the landing leg, the COM will have to travel farther prior to takeoff. The effect is slowed hip rotation and additional braking forces.

To overcome the braking force and keep the COM moving forward, the hamstring must produce greater muscular effort to support the body as it continues to travel over the foot in the up/down and forward direction **(Fig. 15)**. This requires more contractile force and the ability to rapidly absorb energy in the hamstrings. This action is often the culprit in hamstring injuries.

Figure 15 – To keep the COM moving forward, the hamstring must produce greater muscular effort to support the body as it travels.

The athlete who is intentionally trying to increase stride length by "reaching" will quickly fall into this INCORRECT body position and situation.

Visibly, the athlete will appear to be lifting the knee as they complete the recovery phase of the stride cycle, have a low back kick, and may be "sitting" as they run.

COM in Front of the Landing Leg - INCORRECT TECHNIQUE

When the pelvis is tilted backward and the athlete's torso is too far forward, *the COM is positioned in front of the landing leg* **(Fig. 13 (b))**. The result is that the athlete must "catch" their body with the landing foot and leave the ground prematurely. This means there is less time to apply force to the ground.

Visually, the athlete may appear to be leaning forward or bent over and/or may have a high back kick.

COM Above the Landing Leg - CORRECT TECHNIQUE

When the pelvis is upright and above the landing leg, it is easier to run faster **(Fig. 13 (c))**. Maximum force can be applied to the ground – in the correct direction - with optimal ground contact time, delivering a longer, faster stride.

First, the correct body position allows for optimal angle of takeoff and will deliver optimal stride length because *the location of the COM relative to the ground AND the angle of the body* dictate vertical and horizontal components of each stride.

The athlete projects their body forward and upward into the next stride.

If takeoff is too horizontal, a shorter stride will result since the body won't have enough time to travel through the air. If takeoff is too vertical, the body will move up and down more than forward.

The optimal body position allows the body to travel forward farther before it begins to descend back to the ground.

Second, as shown in **Figure 13(c)**, when the pelvis is upright the COM is positioned above the landing leg. In this situation, *the hips are free to rotate around their full range of motion as the hip joint extends*. When the hip joint is undergoing full extension the hip flexors are stretched to "spring" the leg forward during takeoff, utilizing the force-enhancing mechanisms of muscle-tendon stretch and the stretch reflex that we discussed in Chapter 1. The hip joint is high enough off the ground to allow the knee to straighten, the foot to open slightly, then the leg to fold and swing forward. *The rapid forward swing occurs as a result.*

If these available mechanisms are utilized properly, *the athlete won't feel the need to voluntarily lift the knee* in order to clear the ground to correctly make the next stride. If the athlete tries to lift the knee, they may actually disrupt the natural flow of energy storage and release that facilitates rapid leg swing. There's a loss of energy, a loss of mechanical efficiency and thus, a loss of rotational speed.

COACHES NOTE

When running, the ideal position of the body is upright. Visually, the torso might appear a few degrees forward from vertical. Always keep the torso directly over the hips, with the head balanced in a straight line at the top of the spine as an extension of the torso.

Demonstrate the importance of body position and torso alignment by trying each of the options described above. Make sure the athlete feels the difference when their body position is correct.

Arm Stroke Controls Range of Motion in the Stride and Tempo

Proper coordination of the body's lever systems is key to speed development for all athletes. That said, while the fundamental mechanics are the same, the arm stroke technique that generates MAXIMUM speed for the sprinter is significantly different than what is required for the distance runner. It is more explosive in its range of motion, has a much faster tempo and includes significant changes in pendulum length. The competitive distance runner who needs to sprint to the finish will also want to master this technique.

One contribution that the arms offer is to maintain balance. The arm stroke helps the athlete stay balanced over their COM, which allows the athlete to use all available force to drive the body forward. Demonstrate the effect of the arm stroke on balance by asking the athlete to try running with the same arm and leg going forward each time.

They will quickly notice how the body moves from side to side and rotates in an exaggerated motion.

COACHES NOTE

The correct arm stroke enables greater takeoff distance and optimizes the athlete's stride length.

Here's how it works for sprinters:

The arm's downward stroke should increase its pendulum length. This will increase its linear displacement, the torque required to move it AND the resultant centripetal acceleration which translates to a greater force that will be applied to the ground by the opposite leg. Extending the arm on the downward stroke also increases the stretch of the hip flexors on the opposite leg, which exploits the additional force-enhancing mechanisms in the hips.

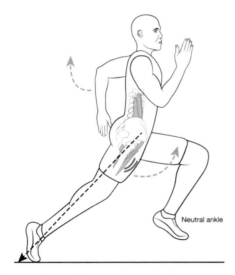

Neutral ankle

In the example shown in **Figure 16**, the left arm has swung down, then back as the right hip flexors stretch and the extensors contribute to applying force to the ground. From there, flexing the elbow on the upstroke reduces the pendulum length and its resistance to movement, which increases its angular velocity. This helps with the swing through of the recovery leg and preparation for the next stride.

Figure 16 – Full hip extension optimizes force applied to the ground.

The arms lead the tempo of the legs, and closing the elbow on the upstroke creates and maintains the athlete's fastest turnover in the legs.

To demonstrate this, let's return to the example we used in Chapter 1: a straight, pendulum-like arm would be much harder to swing. The effect of a straight arm is a much slower swing, too slow for coordinating the legs when running and sprinting at top speed. Not only that, a straight arm on the upstroke would alter the athlete's COM and they would need to reach with the opposite leg in order to compensate. Try it.

The arm's position in relation to the opposite leg is also very important. *The arm strokes and leg strides need to be synchronized in time and movement.*

Visually, they become a mirror image of each other as the athlete gains and/or maintains speed **(Fig. 17)**.

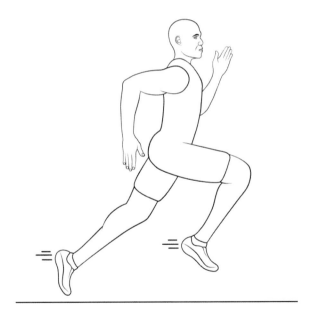

Figure 17 - The arm stroke and leg stride mirror each other.

Finally, while frequency will increase as the athlete accelerates, the athlete should follow through with every arm stroke to make sure that *arm stroke range of motion doesn't change.*

The Actions of the Correct Arm Stroke

The correct arm stroke sequence for the sprinter includes full range of motion and significant changes in pendulum length. Extending the elbow on the downstroke increases the force applied to the ground by the opposite leg. Flexing the elbow on the upstroke increases the angular velocity of the swing leg as it cycles though and prepares for the next stride.

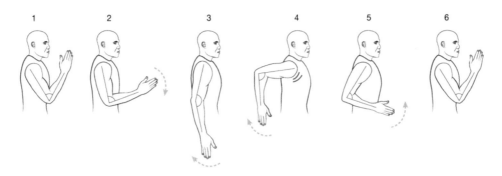

Figure 18 – The correct arm stroke sequence for the sprinter includes full range of motion, significant changes in pendulum length and force-enhancing mechanism at the shoulder.

Figure 18 depicts the correct arm stroke for the sprinter and they are detailed below. The first four images depict the down–then-back swing, and the last two images show the return of the arm to the starting position.

1. The hand is positioned shoulder-high (not above the chin), and slightly in front of the chest. The hand position should peak about 10 inches in front of the chin.

2. The forearm and hand initiate the downward stroke by moving downward while the upper arm rotates backwards from the shoulder.

3. The elbow joint extends to increase the angle between the forearm and upper arm. *This action is what lengthens the pendulum and increases the moment arm*

4. After the hand passes by the hip, the elbow joint begins to flex again and drives backward and upward while the shoulder continues to rotate through its full range of motion. The elbow finishes at 90 degrees, with the forearm directed down to the ground.

COACHES NOTE

At the completion of the downstroke, there should be a "catch" as the elbow reaches its finishing point at 90 degrees. This initiates the force-enhancing mechanisms from the shoulder's muscle-tendon system that causes the arm to rapidly reverse directions.

5. *The hand remains in line, maintaining the length of the pendulum.* The ideal position of the hand is neutral and in line with the forearm so the fingers become a natural extension of the pendulum.

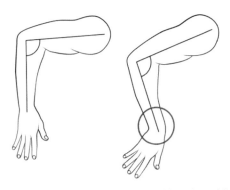

Figure 19 – Close-up of the wrist and hand position.
Fingers should remain in line with the wrist, as shown on the left.

As shown in **Figure 19**, some athletes will let the wrist flail as they bring the arm back. This may give them the false sense that they are reaching the 90-degree finish point. The forward swing is a reversal of this process, except the elbow DOES NOT extend as it passes by the hip. Instead, *the elbow closes from 90 degrees as it swings into the upstroke.* Visually, the elbow is closed with an angle approximating 45 degrees.

6. The pre-stretch and stretch reflex mechanisms at the shoulder cause a rapid return of the arm. The objective of the upstroke is to return to the starting position and STOP, which then prepares the arm to reverse directions for the next down stroke.

The athlete's shoulders, forearms and chest should remain as relaxed as possible.

Some athletes have a tendency to let the arms excessively cross the body in front **(Fig. 20 v. Fig. 21)**. While this may counterbalance any angular momentum that's generated by the swinging legs, it can create too much torso rotation. This would inhibit the correct application of force to the ground.

 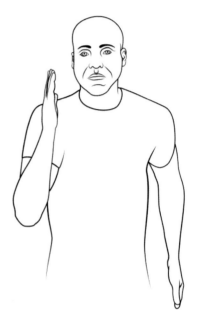

Figure 20 – Excessive cross-over.   **Figure 21 – Correct arm stroke.**

To exaggerate the concept, excessive cross of the arms drives the body in a zig-zag motion, which will prevent the legs from being able to direct the ground force down and back for maximum takeoff. Instead, a portion of the foot force must be used to stop the rotation and send the body back in the opposite direction. In other words, *crossing the arms too much can waste energy.*

As a reminder, the purpose and mechanics of the arm stroke are the same for all running athletes, except that range of motion and changes in pendulum length will be lessened as distance targets increase. Specific details for distance runners are covered in Chapter 4. Note that the competitive distance runner WILL use the explosive arm stroke of a sprinter in order to maximize momentum as they approach the finish line.

Stride Cycle Correctly Applies Force to the Ground During Each Step

Figure 22 – The stride cycle.
Travel distances during the support and aerial phases are not to scale.

As we have discussed, the running technique that creates the most speed consists of a series of impulses that will change and maximize the body's momentum. Each stride consists of two steps, the first being the initial "push" from the ground, and the second being the landing and subsequent push **(Fig. 22)**. The steps consist of a series of impulses, with each impulse being the product of *force applied to the ground and the total time the force is applied.*

Back to the formulas from Chapter 1:

$$\text{Since} \quad \text{Force} \quad = \text{Mass X Acceleration}$$
$$\text{and} \quad \text{Acceleration} \quad = \frac{\Delta \text{ velocity}}{\Delta \text{ time}}$$

we can substitute as follows:

$$\text{Force X } \Delta \text{ time} \quad = \text{Mass x } \Delta \text{ velocity}$$

Assuming body mass remains constant,

$$\text{Impulse} \quad = \text{Force x Time}$$

Therefore, in order to increase impulse, the athlete should either increase force and/or time of ground contact. Further, an increase in force applied to the ground – in the same amount of time – will lead to a greater change in the athlete's momentum.

In the context of running and sprinting, the application of force in the correct direction will increase an athlete's forward momentum.

COACHES NOTE

As momentum increases, time of ground contact decreases with each step. Therefore, it is crucial to continually and correctly apply force to the ground to optimize the forces generated - in the amount of time available – in order to maximize speed and then maintain it for as long as possible.

An analogy that will demonstrate this would come from pushing a car **(Fig. 23)**. The first few strides are very difficult and slow: Even with the high degree of force you apply to the ground, the car barely moves. You continue to push from the back of the car, your legs applying force DOWN and BACK, slowly and deliberately.

As you continue to apply force to the ground, the car builds speed and momentum. Your strides become quicker, you spend less time on the ground, and both you and the car start to move faster. If you continue to apply force, you will soon be running behind the car.

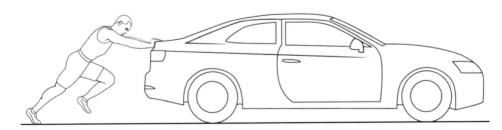

Figure 23 - The first few strides are forceful and deliberate.
Application of force is down and back.

Summary of the Correct Running Stride and Leg Cycle

Refer to **Figure 24** as we review the running stride and leg cycle:

1. At landing, the foot is directly under the COM, with the ankle remaining in a neutral position.

2. A slight and natural flexion of the knee occurs during the landing.

3. Between landing and just prior to takeoff, the leg muscles are active and contributing to the force being applied to the ground. In turn, the ground reaction force pushes on the COM, lifting it up and forward off the ground.

4. As the COM passes over the foot, the hip joint of the landing leg begins to extend.

5. The force-enhancing mechanisms *(pre-stretch and stretch reflex at the hip)* now cause the trailing leg to swing forward automatically at a rapid speed.

6. The knee joint naturally flexes, bringing the calf close to the hamstring, as the knee leads the forward swing. The foot comes through high as part of *shortening the pendulum length,* which allows the leg to swing through faster.

7. As the thigh of the swing leg reaches its maximum forward position, the knee joint begins to extend in preparation for the next landing.

8. *The foot is once again directed to the ground,* with the ankle remaining in a neutral position.

9. Note the undulation of the COM from landing through takeoff.

Figure 24 – The running stride and leg cycle.

The Elements of the Stride Cycle

Stride Frequency

Stride frequency is the number of strides the athlete takes per second. As the athlete correctly applies force to the ground, a change in the athlete's forward momentum will coincide with an increase in stride frequency. This is how the athlete accelerates.

There's an important point here. If the athlete is in the correct body position, stride frequency will increase as the athlete increases velocity. However, ground contact time will decrease. What this means is that *in order to increase and then maintain speed, the athlete must continue to correctly apply force to the ground.*

COACHES NOTE

The correct application of force should cause the athlete to feel like they are pressing the ground. It will feel slower but the athlete must trust that the force-enhancing mechanisms (the muscle-tendon stretch and stretch reflex action) will naturally move the leg forward and upward much faster than if they consciously tried to do it.

The consistent and correct application of force will generate a natural increase in velocity and stride frequency and will optimize acceleration.

The process of increasing stride frequency should be smooth and seamless. We discuss this concept further in Chapter 3 as we apply these mechanics to the sprinting race strategy, specifically during Block Clearance, Acceleration and speed Maintenance.

Stride Length

Stride length is the distance that the athlete's COM travels between consecutive foot contacts, i.e. from initial contact of the right foot to the next initial contact of the left foot. It varies from athlete to athlete and becomes like a fingerprint because the distance any athlete can cover is determined by leg length AND the magnitude and direction of force they apply to the ground.

Stride length is a result of forces applied to the ground and the upper body's position relative to the legs. Stride length can be broken into three components – **Takeoff Distance, Flight Distance** and **Landing Distance (Fig, 25).**

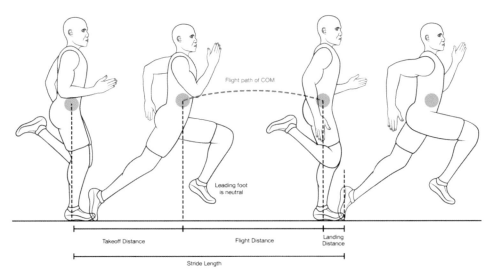

Figure 25 – The elements of stride length. Flight distance is affected by takeoff velocity. Note that COM undulation will occur as a result of application of force.

Takeoff Distance is the horizontal distance the COM travels between landing and the instant when the foot leaves the ground. In this phase of the stride, the correct body position allows for optimal takeoff angle and application of force against the ground. When the pelvis is upright, the COM is positioned above the landing leg and *the hips are free to rotate through their full range of motion as the hip joint extends.* Force is applied in a *downward and slightly backward direction.* The hip flexors undergo stretch as the *hip joint fully extends*, then are released to "spring" the leg forward at takeoff, utilizing the force-enhancing mechanisms of muscle-tendon stretch and the stretch reflex that we discussed in Chapter 1. This is how the athlete maximizes angular velocity of the leg and, ultimately, takeoff velocity.

Flight Distance is the horizontal distance the COM travels in the aerial phase. The objective is to maximize how far the body travels in the forward direction before it begins to descend to the ground. Flight distance is primarily determined by:

1. Velocity at takeoff
2. Relative height of the COM at takeoff
3. Upper body position
4. Air resistance
5. Acceleration due to gravity

Landing Distance is the horizontal distance between the COM and the landing foot at the instant it makes contact with the ground. As discussed earlier, the ideal body configuration positions the COM directly above the landing foot, so *landing distance should be short*. This will minimize braking forces that ultimately decelerate the body. Further, if the foot comes down too far in front of the COM, the foot will spend more time on the ground, slow hip rotation and cause a loss in momentum.

Figure 26 shows the difference between an INCORRECT and a CORRECT landing.

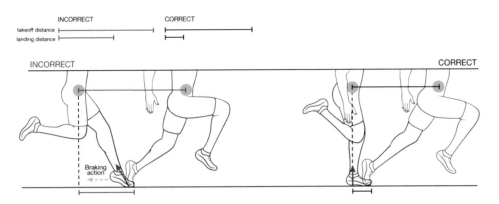

Figure 26 – The visual comparison of the foot landing too far in front of the COM vs. the foot landing directly beneath the COM.

In the INCORRECT example, landing distance – the position of the COM relative to the foot - is increased. The COM is behind the landing foot. There are several consequences:

- Less force being applied to the ground in the correct direction. The ground will push UP and BACKWARD on the athlete, rather than directly UPWARD toward the COM.

- Unnecessary braking forces will slow hip rotation and inhibit takeoff velocity. Note that **takeoff velocity** is the velocity at which the COM is projected upward and forward, and is critical in determining Flight Distance, similar to the concept of projectile motion.

In the INCORRECT landing, the hip will have to cover more distance as it travels over the foot.

Optimal hip rotation is crucial to increasing and sustaining speed.

- Limited knee flexion that naturally occurs on landing inhibits activation of the leg muscles required for application of force. This "ballistic" action of the quadriceps must occur to maximize takeoff velocity and flight distance.

- As discussed earlier, in order to overcome the braking forces and keep the COM moving forward, the hamstring has to produce greater muscular effort to pull the body over the foot to continue cycling forward **(Fig. 27)**. Pulling the body forward and the leg through requires more contractile force and the ability to rapidly absorb energy in the hamstrings, potentially increasing the athlete's risk of injury.

Figure 27 – Foot landing in front of the COM places extra strain on the hamstring muscles, increasing risk of injury.

COACHES NOTE

Positioning the foot too far forward may increase the athlete's perceived stride length, but it is inefficient and can lead to injury. The CORRECT landing, with the COM positioned above the foot and the shank perpendicular to the ground, allows the athlete to optimize hip rotation, application of force in the correct direction, takeoff velocity and, ultimately stride length. DO NOT REACH.

Rather than reaching, improve the elasticity and strength of the legs. Elasticity allows the legs to move freely through their full range of motion and respond to the forces being applied most efficiently. Increasing muscular strength enables more force to be applied to the ground with each stride - as long as the athlete continues to push.

The Correct Landing and Takeoff that Optimize Application of Force

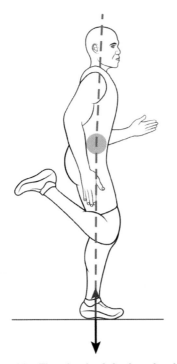

The location of the COM upon landing is key to the athlete's ability to optimize application of force to the ground and maximize stride length on every stride.

The ideal orientation of the leg shank is perpendicular to the ground **(Fig. 28)**.

As a consequence of this particular leg orientation and application of force against the ground, the forces are generated along the leg UPWARD, directly toward the COM.

Figure 28 – The shank of the leg should be perpendicular to the ground upon landing.

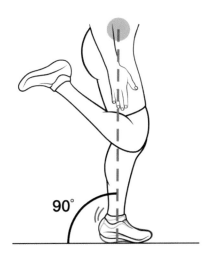

Note that in the sprinting stride and after the start, the foot lands on the mid-section of the ball of the foot and the leg is loaded as the COM passes over the foot. *As the COM passes over the foot (takeoff distance)*, the heel briefly touches the ground, then rises naturally as the athlete's toes are the last to leave the ground **(Fig. 29)**.

Figure 29 – The heel naturally touches the ground as the COM passes over the foot.

COACHES NOTE

The heel touch is not to be focused on in any form of running. It is a *natural* reaction that occurs as the foot and the rest of the leg is loaded. When it comes to the foot strike, the coaching point of emphasis should be to put the foot down underneath you. You cannot think of every segment, i.e. the ball of foot landing, leg loading up, etc. Coach it simply as putting the foot down.

On landing, the foot will stop momentarily. As long as it lands under the COM, it sets up the optimal body position for takeoff, but contributes very little to the actual takeoff.

One more thing :for sprinters: *At full contact of the support leg, both thighs are in the same plane as the heel comes close to the buttocks.* From the side, the knees appear to be together, as shown in **Figure 28** and others.

As the athlete moves to takeoff, they should continue to maintain an upright body position, focus on application of force to the ground and allow the hips to extend.

COACHES NOTE

As the athlete moves from landing to takeoff, they should feel the hip flexors stretch as the hip joint fully extends. The hip extensors at the back of the leg are directing the foot to the ground, but the athlete will not feel them working.

For further detail on how to reinforce this important element of the stride cycle, see the Drills in Chapter 5.

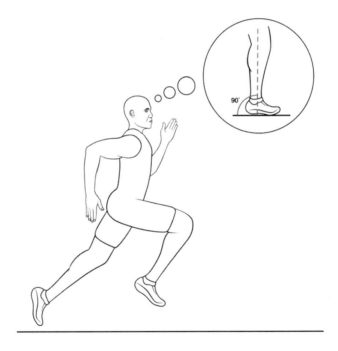

Figure 30 – Lead with the knee and focus on putting the foot straight down. Keep the foot angle neutral.

COACHES NOTE

The athlete should lead with the knee and put the foot straight down - with the shank perpendicular to the ground. Body position must remain upright.

Do not attempt to "lift with the knee".

Summary

Body position, arm stroke and stride cycle are the three fundamental elements of running technique. While they can be studied, practiced and evaluated independently, they are completely interrelated. Proper execution of these elements will determine how fast – and how far – the athlete will run. Not only are they key to mechanical efficiency and speed, they are also essential for safety and injury prevention.

Body position is the most important of the three because it either facilitates or inhibits range of motion in the hips and the application of force in the correct direction - which is downward and slightly backward. Complete hip rotation enables maximum takeoff velocity in the stride and this is what delivers optimal stride length. The athlete needs to stay upright, with the head and torso in line. Watch the chin to make sure the head remains balanced and doesn't fall backward, as this will pull the torso behind the COM during the run and lead to reaching.

The arm stroke enables equal and opposite action in the legs and will make all the difference in the amount and direction of the force being applied to the ground. Focus on each phase of the arm stroke: make sure the elbow extends as the arm swings downward, feel the "catch" at the shoulder as you swing back and let it come forward. Athletes can practice in the mirror to get it right.

Stride frequency and stride length should be treated more as a result than an intention. With an upright body position and an arm stroke that facilitates force being applied to the ground, the athlete will naturally increase momentum and stride frequency. Add optimal hip rotation and hip extension upon takeoff and the athlete will maximize the distance covered with each stride, without risk of injury.

Chapter 3

Sprinting from Start to Finish

IT'S LIKE A PUZZLE. ALL OF THE SKILLS HAVE TO FIT TOGETHER TO RUN YOUR FASTEST. "

- TOM TELLEZ

Training focus and execution when sprinting require a unique application of the principles of body position, arm stroke and stride cycle. Athletes who want to maximize speed over short distances must focus on *correct and explosive execution of all the variables discussed thus far* – without compromise.

There is almost no margin for error in sprinting. Think of it this way: the difference between running a 100-meter race in 10.00 vs. 10.10 is only 1 percent. This tiny difference in speed could prevent the competitive athlete from making the Final in track and field. In terms of distance covered, this tiny speed deficit could prevent the wide receiver from missing a pass, the cornerback from missing a tackle, or the base runner from making the steal. For young athletes in some of the most popular sports, speed defines TALENT.

Using the 100-meter distance as a platform for discussion, we break down sprinting into phases, discuss the variables within each one, and then apply the correct mechanics to assure optimal execution and race performance. The objective is to make sure coaches and athletes understand what the correct mechanics look like, what to focus on during each step of the sprint and more importantly, why.

The intricate skills required to maximize speed, along with key coaching recommendations that will produce a perfectly executed sprint, are discussed in this chapter.

The Five Phases of Sprinting

The most successful sprinters make their races appear seamless. They come out of the blocks and execute a smooth acceleration, achieve top speed, then attempt to maintain that speed to cross the finish line first. As we watch them race, it's difficult to see how and when these athletes move from one "phase" to the next. However, *the specific details of force application do change from start to finish.*

Regardless of ability, for an athlete to reach their maximum potential as a sprinter, their training should center on these factors:

- Reaction Time (RT)
- Block Clearance (BC)
- Speed of Efficient Acceleration (AC)
- Maintenance of Maximum Velocity (MT)
- Minimized Deceleration (MD)

Having coached the world's fastest athletes, Tom Tellez developed this chart to help others understand the relative importance of these individual factors.

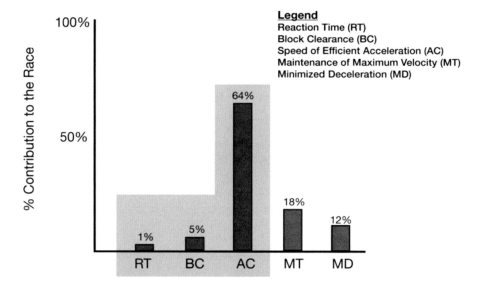

Figure 31 - The phases of the 100-meter race.

The first three factors add up to 70 percent of the race, which equates to 70 meters **(Fig. 31)**. However, since the athlete's ability to accelerate smoothly and efficiently is heavily influenced by the position of the body as they leave the blocks, Block Clearance may be thought of as contributing much more to the total race than the 5% shown.

We will review the essential elements of each phase below.

Reaction Time (RT)

Every race begins with the starter's firing of a pistol that creates a very loud pop. While reaction time is a very small percentage of the overall race, it presents a significant risk factor during competition – and it applies to many sports beyond track.

Athletes must practice "listening for the gun". The risk of anticipating the gun can result in a false start - and disqualification - due to nerves or distraction.

Minimizing reaction time offers a very specific training opportunity that reaches beyond technical mechanics. The objective of this training is to enable conscious relaxation during competition. By desensitizing the athlete to the natural stressors of competition, they can stay focused on execution of their own race. Repetition in practice will be key. Use video to review starts to measure improvement.

COACHES NOTE

Create rituals, like going through the same routine as a way of getting into the blocks at practice and at meets. Repeat the Points of Focus (see Chapter 5) and include them prior to every start. The idea is to establish patterns that are developed in practice that can then carry over to every meet.

Block Clearance (BC)

The primary objective of block clearance mechanics is to establish a balanced body position that enables the athlete to *leave the blocks with the greatest possible velocity and to transition effectively into full sprinting action.*

Here are the objectives of Block Clearance mechanics (refer to **Fig. 32 and Fig. 33)**:

1.   Establish a balanced position.
2.   Get the COM high and slightly forward to enable the athlete to apply force to the blocks and facilitate movement of the COM in the direction of the sprint.
3.   Apply force against the blocks in a straight line leading through the ankle, knee and hip, shoulder and head.
4.   Establish an optimum angle in the rear knee for the rear leg to utilize available force-enhancing mechanisms in the calf and lower leg that will initiate movement and facilitate rapid swinging of the limbs.
5.   Establish an optimum angle in the front knee so the greatest amount of force can be exerted in the least amount of time.
6.   Obtain the optimum angle through the body that maximizes horizontal range yet overcomes gravity so ground contact can be broken.

Let's go back to the physics for just a moment. Block Clearance will determine how well the athlete overcomes *inertia and gravity to increase momentum.*

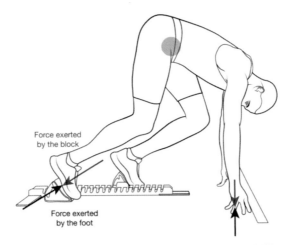

Force exerted
by the block

Force exerted
by the foot

Figure 32 – The forces at work on the body in SET.

At the start, the athlete's mass (entire body) is at rest **(Fig. 32)**. The only external forces acting on the system are the athlete's body weight (due to gravity), the forces from the blocks that push back on the legs and the forces from the ground that push on the arms. If these forces are balanced, i.e., equal and opposite, and there are no other external forces acting upon it, the body will remain at rest. [2]

When the athlete applies force (greater than body weight) to the blocks, inertia and gravity are overcome and forward motion begins. When horizontal and vertical forces are applied equally, the athlete will project at an optimal angle of 45 degrees **(Fig. 33)**.

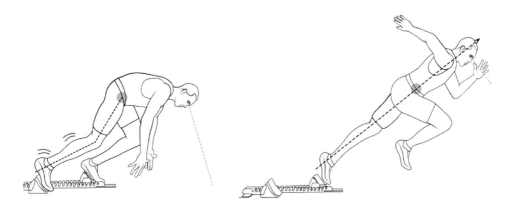

Figure 33 – A successful block clearance creates a 45-degree angle of projection.

COACHES NOTE

The 45-degree angle of projection optimizes application of force, which must become more vertical for the athlete to overcome gravity and break contact with the ground in order to set up a smooth acceleration. Force-enhancing mechanisms in the ankle and calf of the rear leg should be visible as force is applied.

---

[2] Note that wind elements will play a significant role, but for now, we simplify our example by assuming wind resistance is negligible.

Determining the Correct Block Settings

Correct set up is unique to each athlete since no two athletes have the same height, leg or arm length. That said, the same principles apply to everyone.

Figures 34 and 35 depict the specific elements of block placement.

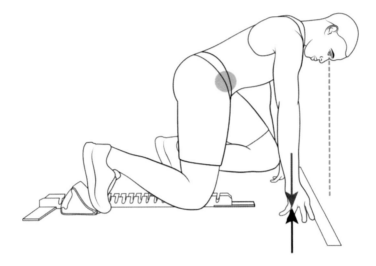

Figure 34 – Side view of the athlete in the blocks.

1. The athlete's strong leg is forward in the blocks. The strong leg is the leg the athlete plants when they kick a ball.

2. The athlete kneels with the front toe adjacent to the rear knee that is on the ground.

3. The knee of the front leg comes to a position that is even with the forearm.

4. The athlete places the hands on the ground so *the hands are directly below the shoulders, with the arms fully extended.*

5. The shank of the front leg is parallel to the ground.

6. The weight of the body should be balanced between the hands and the rear knee that is on the ground.

7. In the front block, the foot is placed so that the toes are resting on the track.

8. In the rear block, the tip of the big toe is just touching the track. The whole foot is on the block.

COACHES NOTE

The objective of foot placement in the blocks is to use the ball of the foot to help push off the block. This position also allows for optimal utilization of the force-enhancing mechanisms available in the lower leg (the pre-stretch and stretch reflex) in the calf and ankle muscle-tendon structures.

9. From the front, the hands appear to be "bridged", with the fingers spread. From the side, the arms look perpendicular to the ground.

10. The head and neck are held comfortably in natural alignment with the spine. Note that the focus of the eyes should be downward on the track.

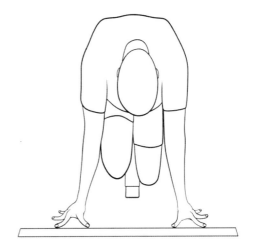

Figure 35 – Front view of the athlete in the blocks.

Getting to the right block settings takes some practice and repetition from the SET position. Adjustments may need to be made to assure optimum positioning. The key objective here is to establish a balanced and relaxed position. If the athlete is uncomfortable in this position, something is not correct.

COACHES NOTE

To establish a baseline for block settings:
1. Place the front of the block 1 foot-length from the starting line.
2. Place the forward pedal 1-1/2 foot-lengths from the starting line.
3. Place the rear pedal 3 foot-lengths from the starting line.

The Optimal SET Position

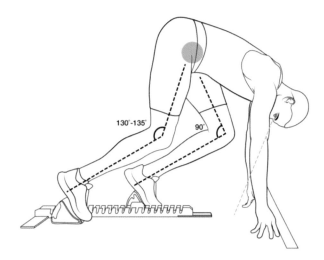

Figure 36 – Optimal leg angles in SET facilitate application of force.

The athlete smoothly raises the hips as high as possible while keeping the shoulders above the hands. The position of the athlete's COM must feel balanced while also being coupled with optimal knee angles to facilitate the greatest application of force in the correct direction. The objective is to *generate the largest ground reaction force that will project the body's COM with the greatest velocity, which will allow the athlete to transition effectively into full sprinting action.*

Referring to **Figure 36**, here are the specifics:

1. The front and rear leg muscles should be in a set and relaxed position, but with just enough contractile tension to support the body in the correct SET position during the start.

2. The optimal angles show the front knee maintaining a 90-degree angle. This angle will maximize the force produced concentrically by the front leg's quadriceps femoris (knee extension) and hamstrings (thigh extension) during the start. *There is no pressure on the front block in the SET position.*

   If the angle of the front leg is smaller, the COM is too low, and the athlete will have a more difficult time extending the hip of the front leg to project their body at the optimal 45-degree angle.

3. A 130- or 135-degree angle in the rear leg allows enough flexion in the knee so that force can also be applied against the rear block as the knee quickly extends during the start. At this angle the height of the COM will help the athlete maximize and optimize the direction of the total force that is applied to both blocks to propel the body.

Remember, the objective is to enable the athlete to produce the greatest amount of force in the least amount of time in order to facilitate a rapid change in their momentum.

4. *Both ankles should be close to neutral* at 90-degree angles so the athlete can put more pressure on the rear block and obtain maximum value from the lower leg's force- enhancing mechanisms (**Fig. 37 and Fig. 38**).

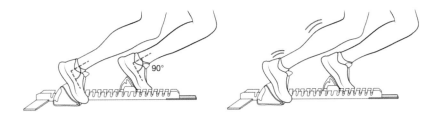

Figure 37 and Figure 38. Foot and ankle position in SET. Ankles should be close to 90 degrees to facilitate force-enhancing mechanisms.

The pre-stretch / stretch reflex mechanisms at the Achilles tendon and calf muscle enable the rear leg to move through a greater range of motion at a higher angular velocity.

COACHES NOTE

Utilization of the force-enhancing mechanisms in the rear leg is crucial to a productive start. This may be a reason for not using high-back block pedals, which inhibit the stretch of the calf. This can limit the storage and release of elastic energy in the tendon which may limit the amount of force the athlete can apply to the block.

5. *The degree of forward lean should be minimal and slightly forward, and the head should remain in natural alignment with the torso* **(Fig. 39)**. This position allows the athlete to feel the correct pressure against the rear block and allows the shoulders to rise efficiently at the gun with the head and upper body in unison.

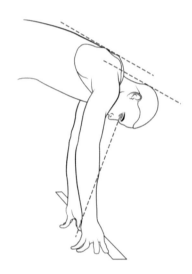

Figure 39 – Head and torso alignment, line of sight in SET.

If the degree of forward lean is too great, additional pressure on the hands will prevent the athlete from leaving the blocks balanced and under control. It also makes it very difficult to project the body at a 45-degree angle and correctly apply force to the blocks. The consequence will be quick, short strides instead of the *deliberate, forceful strides that lead to efficient and maximum acceleration*. Too little forward lean in the SET position can cause the athlete to prematurely stand up out of the blocks. This creates a stalling effect which prevents the COM from moving forward in the direction of the run.

To accomplish the correct degree of forward lean, the eyes should now be focused on a point between the athlete's hands and front foot.

COACHES NOTE

While the initial strides out of the blocks should be deliberate and forceful, the athlete must remain relaxed and not feel tight or tense.

KEEP THE CHEST RELAXED.

When in the SET position, many inexperienced athletes keep their focus on the same point as the "to your marks" position. Consequently, tension will be evident in the back of the neck. Another common error is the athlete who looks down the track at the finish line. This may cause them to stay low at the gun. DO NOT LOOK UP WHEN IN THE BLOCKS.

Taken together, these actions allow the athlete to apply maximum force to the blocks – in the correct direction - increasing the force that can be applied to the COM for maximum velocity out of the blocks.

COACHES NOTE

While the SET position is held for a very short time, it's critical to get it right. Take the time to photograph your athletes in SET. Shoot from a side angle and study what needs to be changed. Practice until the athlete achieves the correct SET position every time.

Once the athlete's SET position body angles are correct, and the start looks and feels right at the "Gun", the last step is to use a tape measure and note the distance from the line to the front block and from the line to the back block (**Fig. 40**). *These dimensions become the athlete's personal and unique block settings.*

Figure 40 – Each athlete should know their unique block measurements.

COACHES NOTE

Block equipment can vary at every competition. Help the athlete learn to set their own blocks correctly by learning their unique settings and creating a disposable "tape measure" they can bring to every event. Knowing their correct measurements assures precision and eliminates risk of variability on race day.

Block Clearance – The Mechanical Sequence

Once the athlete has the correct block settings, there is a specific sequence to study and train. The details to emphasize are below (**Fig. 41**).

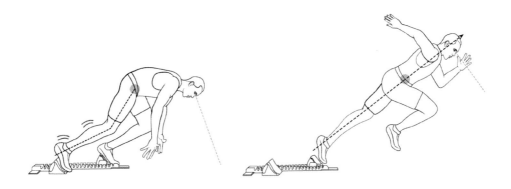

Figure 41 – Apply force to both blocks, achieve full hip extension, get to a 45-degree angle of projection, keep the head and torso aligned.

"The GUN" and the First Three Strides

Hips, legs and feet. At the gun, as force is exerted against both blocks, the trunk begins to rise as the front leg fully extends. Reviewing the discussion from Chapters 1 and 2, *the athlete should focus on full extension of the hip*, while initially keeping the knee and ankle in a neutral position so that they can engage the force-enhancing mechanisms acting at the calf to naturally move the rear foot forward. The rear leg's foot takes the shortest path to the front of the body as the COM rises and moves forward.

Hips, legs and feet action from the blocks should emphasize *pushing backward and downward* at a 45-degree angle of projection, pushing off the heel back onto the ball of both feet. This will deliver an equal horizontal and vertical force in one direct line through the body, allowing the athlete to overcome inertia and gravity, continue to rise and get into a position to accelerate. The motion is piston-like as the athlete applies force from a resting state.

On the first step out of the blocks and as the rear leg's foot moves forward and prepares to land, the shin will appear to be at 45 degrees relative to the ground. The ankle joint should be held in a neutral position **(Fig. 42)**.

COACHES NOTE

The first stride out of the blocks will be the most deliberate and the shortest. This is because the body's mass is in a resting state, so its resistance to movement is high. The athlete will require more time to push off the blocks and generate a large enough force to initiate movement of the body's mass. As a consequence, it takes more time complete the first stride and thus, stride frequency is low and the initial stride length is short. Refer to Appendix D for a visual demonstration.

Figure 42 – The optimal position of the rear leg's shin and ankle on the first step out of the block.

COACHES NOTE

As the foot lands, the athlete should position it directly under the body's COM. The foot is there for support only. Ground contact should be on the ball of the foot or mid-foot for the first three strides. The heel will not touch down. As the body rises, the heel will naturally come down as shown in Appendix D.

Body and head position. The head should always be in line with the shoulders and torso. At the start, the torso rises at 45 degrees, following the line of the spine. As the torso becomes more upright, the head moves too, but *the head always stays in line with the torso* (**Fig. 43**).

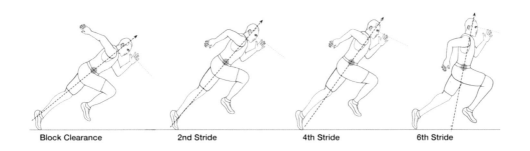

Block Clearance   2nd Stride   4th Stride   6th Stride

**Figure 43 – The athlete should rise smoothly from the start to an upright body position,
which takes approximately 6 strides in the 100 meter race.
This enables the most efficient acceleration.**

Arm stroke at the start. Arm stroke is critical to maximizing the force applied to the blocks. The elbows stay close to the body (medially) and the arms act independently from the shoulders, as though the upper arm was connected by a pin to the shoulder and was free to move. The path of the arm opposite the front knee is backward: the elbow angle continues to open as the hand approaches the hip area, then begins to close as it passes the hip. The other arm swings forward and the elbow angle continues to close. Overall, *the arm action matches the opposite leg action in force and range of motion.* Visually, the opposite arm and leg should look similar to each other.

First three strides. With the correct arm stroke at the start, the athlete will achieve a greater takeoff distance, which naturally enhances stride length. At the start, when resistance is at its highest, it takes longer to go through the stride cycle, so stride frequency is going to be low.

COACHES NOTE

The first three strides at the start are deliberate and forceful. The athlete should focus on application of force against the ground. A good visual analogy to use for the first three strides is pushing a car from a dead stop.

Efficient Acceleration (AC)

With a correct start, the athlete has the best opportunity for efficient acceleration. *The objective of the acceleration phase is to cover the longest possible distance in the least amount of time.*

Assuming the start is mechanically correct and successful, the acceleration phase should flow smoothly and gradually. The *application of forces that increase stride length and stride speed are a progression* that continues as the body rises into the sprinting position.

Since maximum speed can only be carried for 1 to 2 seconds, an athlete who accelerates too quickly will be decelerating over a longer portion of the race while others are still accelerating. Too often, there is a tendency toward trying to be quick, and this sacrifices stride length and power for turnover. The athlete must find the optimal stride length and turnover rate to allow for the greatest efficiency over the given distance of the race.

COACHES NOTE

As the athlete comes up to full sprinting position and momentum builds, stride frequency will increase and strides will lengthen naturally.

As stride frequency increases, *the force applied to the ground is directed more downward than backward* as the body comes up to reach full sprinting position. As the athlete accelerates, the shin of the landing leg will appear to be at 90 degrees relative to the ground.

The athlete's **body position** dictates how reactive forces affect the motion of the whole body's COM. *The neck and head continue to remain in a natural alignment throughout the run.*

As discussed, ground reaction forces should be directed primarily UPWARD upon landing to enable optimal hip rotation and continued application of force to maximize the takeoff **(Fig. 44)**.

Therefore, *the athlete should be applying force mostly downward and very slightly backward.*

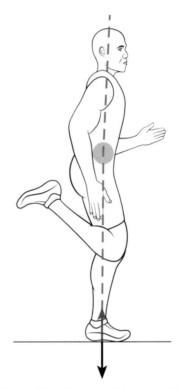

Figure 44 – The correct body position and landing optimizes hip rotation and application of force.

The **arm stroke** during Acceleration follows the pattern initiated during Block Clearance. The elbow joint extends during the downward arm stroke, which lengthens the pendulum and increases the moment arm **(Fig. 45a)**. This action increases the arm's ability to produce centripetal acceleration, which translates to a greater force that can be applied to the ground by the opposite leg. If the arm swings back properly (ideal position highlighted in black), it will elicit and utilize the force-enhancing mechanisms that arise from stretch of muscle-tendon structures in the shoulder. The increase in force will accelerate the arm forward in a "spring-like" manner so that the elbow naturally closes on the upward (recovery) phase of the arm stroke, helping to facilitate a faster turnover in the legs **(Fig. 45b)**. *Closing the elbow on the upstroke helps the athlete create and maintain the fastest turnover in the legs.*

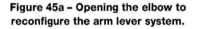

Figure 45a – Opening the elbow to reconfigure the arm lever system.

Figure 45b – Closing the elbow to reconfigure the arm lever system.

Here is the correct arm stroke sequence that was introduced in Chapter 2 **(Fig. 46)**.

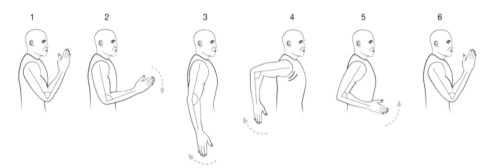

Figure 46 – The sequence of the correct arm stroke.

COACHES NOTE

The athlete MUST go through the correct arm stroke sequence with every stride in order to maximize acceleration.

Each **leg stride** should leverage a complete range of motion, with each landing directly under the athlete's COM **(Fig. 47)**.

Figure 47 – The leg stride for smooth and efficient acceleration maximizes range of motion, optimizes pendulum length changes and muscle-tendon stretch mechanisms.

Note that strides become quicker through the full range of motion as the athlete builds momentum and achieves maximum speed.

Maintaining Maximum Velocity (MT)

Analysis of some of the world's fastest athletes shows that 100-meter sprinters reach maximum velocity between 60 and 70 meters and can only maintain it for 4 to 5 strides.

The muscle groups involved in each stride undergo a lightning fast switch from contraction to relaxation. The athlete's secret is their ability to sustain this switch skillfully

COACHES NOTE

Once the athlete achieves maximum velocity, the objective is to maintain it, NOT to increase it. The athlete must stay relaxed, continue to stroke the arms and correctly apply force against the ground.

At this point, the arm stroke and leg stride are in perfect sync, and the athlete goes through the full range of motion in both the arms and legs. Visually, the arms mirror the legs **(Fig. 48)**.

Figure 48 – Arms and legs are in sync and completing their full range of motion.

Why does an athlete slow down after achieving maximum velocity? The answer is there is a physiological limit to how long an athlete can sustain maximum velocity.

First, as momentum increases, the time the leg has to produce force on the ground decreases. And second, the muscles in the body have begun to fatigue and will have a hard time producing the forces necessary to sustain top speed. As a result, the force generated with each stride will weaken, and the athlete will begin a gradual, unnoticed deceleration.

Another factor is body position. When the body's horizontal momentum becomes greater than that of the legs, the body starts toppling over, causing a greater braking action each time the foot hits the ground.

COACHES NOTE

Athletes may ask, "How will I know when I've reached top speed?" At top speed, it will feel like they are shifting from 5th to 6th gear, and they are about to either go into overdrive or topple over. To keep this from happening, they should continue to stroke the arms, relax, and let momentum take their body to the finish line.

Minimized Deceleration (MD)

The athlete who decelerates the least wins the race.

Correct technique minimizes deceleration during the final meters. The athlete should continue to stroke the arms through their complete range of motion, remain upright, lead with the knee and put the foot down under their whole body's COM on every stride.

By this time in the race, fatigue and the stress of competition can create significant consequences. Mastery of effective relaxation technique helps the athlete maintain correct and smooth form and prevents unnecessary muscle tightening during the final meters of the race.

Everything else being equal, the athlete who is superior in anaerobic conditioning will "slow down the least".

The chest stays relaxed, the mouth stays open through the finish.

Summary

Successful athletes appear smooth and relaxed in every phase of a race - from start to finish. The 100-meter distance offers the opportunity to focus on every phase because there is no margin for error. The 100-meter athlete must optimize magnitude and direction of forces applied to ground with every stride.

Combining the correct block settings, SET position and deliberate, forceful block clearance mechanics enable the athlete to overcome gravity and inertia. They are the foundation of a smooth, seamless and optimized acceleration, so are crucial to a successful race. Achieving maximum speed occurs with correct application of force on every stride and is completely dependent on body position, arm stroke, and an optimized stride cycle that takes advantage of all available mechanisms to move the whole body's COM forward. As stride frequency and stride length naturally increase, the athlete's challenge is to maintain speed for as long as possible by staying relaxed, continuing to stroke the arms, and correctly applying force to the ground. Staying patient as the finish line approaches minimizes deceleration.

Every detail matters.

Chapter 4

Mechanical Differences among Longer Sprints, Distance Running and Standing Starts

---

NO MATTER WHAT THE DISTANCE, MAXIMUM SPEED ALWAYS COMES FROM PROPER APPLICATION OF FORCE IN ORDER TO PROPEL THE BODY FORWARD."

- TOM TELLEZ

Applying the correct technique during phases of the 100-meter race was the focus of Chapter 3. Here we review the mechanics of the longer sprints – the 200-meter and 400-meter races - and describe the slight differences in mechanics and race strategy. We cover block placement, block clearance, running the curves during acceleration and speed maintenance in the 200. In the 400, the athlete must manage tempo and conserve energy, then be ready to sprint the last 100 meters for an explosive finish.

From there, distance running mechanics and race strategy are reviewed. While sprinters focus on explosive movement, maximum range of motion and applying all available force-enhancing mechanisms to optimize each stride, distance runners need to focus on economy and sustaining their energy.

The mechanics for longer distance events have nuances in the start, the arm stroke and the stride cycle. Competitive distance runners might also use sprint mechanics for an explosive finish.

Running the 200-Meter Race

While most of the principles of the 100-meter race also apply to the 200, there are several differences the athlete must execute to run a successful 200-meter race.

Running the Curve

The 200-meter distance includes a curve where additional forces are at work. The athlete's body position will change in relation to the track.

1. Centripetal force acts on a body moving in a circular path and is directed toward the center around which the body is moving **(Fig. 49)**.
2. Tangential force acts on a moving body in the direction of a tangent to the path of the body, its effect being to increase or diminish velocity. It is distinguished from a normal force, which acts at right angles to the tangent and changes the direction of the motion without changing the velocity.

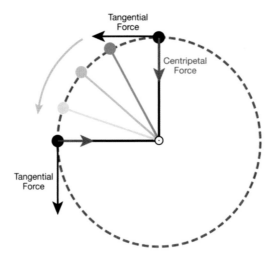

**Figure 49 – Centripetal and tangential forces affect
how the sprinter should run the curve.**

To overcome these forces, the athlete maintains *head-torso-lower body alignment
while running the curve* **(Fig. 50)**. The tighter the curve, the more leaned the body is.
It should be noted that the athlete is leaning into the curve, and *not bent at the
waist*.

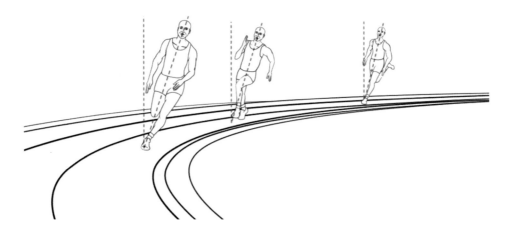

Figure 50 – Head and torso remain in line and leaned while running the curve.

Phases of the 200

Phases of the 200 present some differences from the 100, especially in the start and block clearance details:

1. Since the acceleration phase occurs on the curve of the track, blocks should be placed at a slight angle from the starting line and in the direction of the run **(Fig. 51)**. The athlete's *hands should be placed in line with the blocks, not the starting line* (inset).

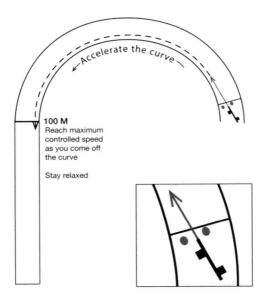

Figure 51 – 200-meter block placement and direction of the start.

2. The 200-meter start is not as explosive as the 100-meter start in terms of application of force and distribution of energy. The first three strides out of the blocks are still deliberate and forceful for maximum acceleration, but the athlete gets into the full sprinting position a little later (around 8 strides) since they are accelerating over a longer distance.

3. The **Acceleration** phase occurs while the athlete is running the curve. The athlete should run approximately 8-12 inches outside the inside lane line to minimize the curve's distance, but must avoid running on the line. Running too far from the inside lane line will increase the distance the athlete must cover, which will create a disadvantage and increase overall performance time.

4. The athlete should reach maximum controlled speed as they come off the curve onto the straightaway. For the last 100 meters, the athlete is in the Maintenance phase of the race. This is when they must relax and try to decelerate as little as possible.

COACHES NOTE

The 200-meter athlete needs to stay relaxed and continue to execute the correct technique: keep the body upright, stroke the arms, lead with the knee to put the feet down under the COM and apply force to the ground. Lastly, let the finish line come to you.

DO NOT REACH.

Except for blocks placement, a longer acceleration and running the curve, the 200-meter sprinter must execute the same start and running mechanics as described in previous chapters.

Running the 400-Meter Race

The 400-meter race is where the changes in technique become more noticeable. At this distance, the athlete is still utilizing the correct running mechanics, but the movements are visibly less explosive than what's needed for the short distances. Economy and conservation of energy become important and are crucial.

1. Block positioning, block settings, and the athlete's overall start technique are the same in the 400 as in the 200-meter race; however, the start is more conservative.

2. The range of motion of the arm stroke and utilization of changes in pendulum length are more conservative in the 400-meter when compared to the 100 and 200-meter races **(Fig. 52)**. While the arm stroke still includes the down-then-back motion, the elbow angle remains consistent throughout.

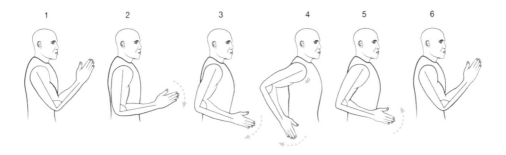

Figure 52 – The 400-meter arm stroke is more conservative than what's needed for the 100 and 200, with smaller changes in pendulum length and a shorter range of motion.

3. The arm stroke continues to control the tempo and range of motion of the stride cycle. To run faster, increase speed and range of motion of the arm stroke.

4. The athlete runs the curves in the same manner described for the 200-meter race.

5. As the athlete enters the final 100 meters of the race, to combat growing fatigue, they should focus on staying tall, relaxed, maintaining the arm stroke and letting the finish line come to them.

400-Meter Race Planning

While there are different race plans available, Coach Tellez designed this plan for the 400-meter distance:

1. The 400-meter athlete should run the first 50 meters to build momentum and find their rhythm, then let that carry them through the first 250 meters. As a gauge of tempo, the athlete should run the first 200 meters slightly slower than their best 200-meter time.

2. At the 250-meter mark, the athlete should take a breath and exhale, stroke the arms through their full range of motion and minimize deceleration by staying relaxed through the finish line.

COACHES NOTE

The 400-meter athlete who trains with the short-distance sprinters will likely optimize their arm stroke and stride frequency during the final phase of the race and achieve their best performance.

Distance Running

We know that the mechanics of human motion and speed development are essentially the same for every athlete; however, there are some very specific differences in technique that apply to distance runners. Distance runners need to focus on economy and sustaining their energy. The mechanics for longer distance events have nuances in the start, arm stroke and stride cycle. Competitive distance runners might also use sprint mechanics for an explosive finish.

Let's review the key points of good technique for distance running.

Mechanics of Body Position, Arm Stroke and Stride Cycle

1. The athlete should run tall, keeping the head and torso in line with the pelvis and hips. The face and jaw muscles should be relaxed, with the mouth open to allow air to enter and carbon dioxide to exit naturally.

2. The athlete should keep the shoulders relaxed, being careful not to raise the shoulders and create tension in the shoulder and neck area.

3. The arms still control hip rotation and stride tempo. The elbow should remain bent at close to 90 degrees with minimal, if any, change in pendulum length. The range of motion of the arm swing will be lessened when running at slower tempos **(Fig. 53)**.

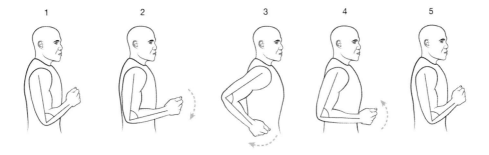

Figure 53 – The arm stroke of the distance runner has minimal change in pendulum length and limited range of motion due to the slower tempo of the race.

Driving the elbows back and up allows a greater take-off distance, which enhances stride length. When the elbow is driven backwards, the force-enhancing mechanisms reviewed in Chapters 1 and 2 will occur at the shoulder to propel the arm forward with a slingshot effect. The faster the athlete runs, and the more explosive the arm stroke, the more this will come into play.

4.   The athlete should not focus on driving the arm and elbow forward; only on the backward motion. The forward motion will happen naturally.

5.   The arm swing comes from the shoulders as the elbow and forearms are relaxed. The fingers are relaxed and the arms may cross the body slightly and move toward the mid-line **(Fig. 54)**.

Figure 54 – Frontal view of the arm stroke of the distance runner.

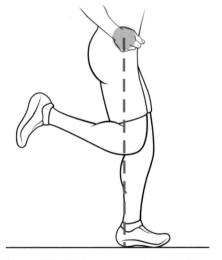

The distance athlete should run with a natural stride, maintain a neutral ankle and not reach the foot forward.

6.   While the foot lands slightly forward of perpendicular, the athlete should not reach to accomplish this **(Fig. 55)**. As discussed in Chapter 2, the foot landing too far in front of the COM causes greater braking forces that will inhibit hip rotation, limit impulse and slow the athlete down.

Figure 55 – Distance runner foot strike.

The knee leads the leg forward, but not as high as the sprinter's, and the COM follows, landing just behind the foot. The orientation of the leg shank is slightly forward of the COM.

7. A significant difference in distance running is how the landing occurs on the foot. Distance runners land closer to mid-foot. The distance runner's landing occurs toward the outside of the foot, then moves to the center with the big toe being the last to leave the ground. The athlete will not feel this, though, as this process occurs within a tenth of a second.

COACHES NOTE

The distance athlete will feel the foot landing as one smooth motion, and emphasis should be placed on putting the foot down underneath the COM. Upon ground contact, the foot and the knee should be in alignment so the shin is perpendicular to the ground.

8. The amount of force applied to the ground and the amount of hip extension are what control speed.

    Arm swing and hip extension should be utilized to control tempo.

    As the athlete runs faster, range of motion should increase.

Remember, *maximum speed always comes from applying force to the ground in the correct direction to propel the body forward.*

Distance Running Track Management, Tempo Control and Race Strategy

To prepare for a competitive race, here are some additional areas of focus:

1. Ensure each athlete has a chance to lead and follow others around the track.

2. After the start, athletes must practice running toward the inside line. There should never be enough space for another runner to pass on the inside; however, the athlete shouldn't run so close to the inside lane line to risk being pushed over. Practice this until it is automatic.

3. The distance athlete should focus on a strong takeoff when going around the curve. The athlete's head-torso-body alignment will be flanged through the curve. Athletes who lean correctly can push against the ground while running on the curve of the track. This allows them to apply force to the ground efficiently and in the correct direction.

4. Regarding tempo, athletes should know what their target lap time feels like on race day. Faster tempo laps that blend with longer, slower laps during practice will help to develop this. By race day, the athlete should have a target tempo and be able to hold that tempo for the entire distance.

5. Remember to ease up on training intensity a few days before a race. This means 2-3 days for a middle-distance race and 4 days before a half- or full marathon.

The Standing Start for Distance Runners and Other Sports

The objectives, principles and execution of a block start also apply to a standing (static) start. The mechanics that lead to the same smooth acceleration pattern can be applied to distance running, field events (such as the jumps and pole vault) and the baseball diamond or football field. The correct body position, utilization of available force-enhancing mechanisms in the forward leg, and the correct arm stroke will maximize velocity as the athlete accelerates.

COACHES NOTE

For the standing start, the athlete leans slightly forward from the waist in order to get the COM a bit forward.

Here are the details **(Fig. 56 and Fig. 57)**:

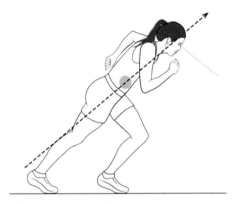

Figure 56 – The standing starting position for distance runners and other sports.

1. The strong leg is forward.

2. The arms can either be relaxed in front (hanging) OR positioned in the runner's arm stroke as shown.

**Figure 57 – The standing start sequence. The athlete maintains head-torso alignment and rises smoothly from the start to an upright body position.
This enables the most efficient acceleration.**

3. The head and torso are in alignment. As with a block start, the eyes are focused at a 45-degree angle looking down, which helps the body propel to the desired 45-degree angle during the first three strides.

4. The push off the front leg should fully extend at the hip to 45 degrees.

5. The arm stroke at the start utilizes greater range of motion to maximize force applied to the ground.

Summary

While the underlying principles of force application and utilization of the lever systems to create speed are the same for all athletes who run, the application of these details is somewhat different for the longer sprints and distance running events. Block placement, block clearance, running the curves during acceleration, and speed maintenance in the 200 are key elements to practice. The 400-meter arm stroke and stride cycle are less explosive because the athlete must manage tempo and conserve energy, so they can be ready to sprint the last 100 meters for an explosive finish. Distance mechanics are even quieter so the athlete can sustain energy. Distance runners use a standing start and may use sprint technique to kick to the finish. Note that all standing starts, whether for track and field events or other sports, still focus on correct application of force that will optimize the desired acceleration and velocity to accomplish the particular objective.

Chapter 5

Changing Habits

and Putting It All Together

COACH WHAT'S CORRECT, AND DON'T CHANGE WHAT'S NOT BROKEN."

- TOM TELLEZ

The principles of motion and their correct application to speed development is complex. As we shared in the Introduction to this book, access to correct and meaningful information is a challenge for coaches. We trust that we have presented these details in a way that makes them easier to understand and that this translates to enabling every athlete to maximize their speed.

Knowing WHAT to do is only half the challenge. HOW to coach the details in a way that helps every athlete optimize performance is the other half. In this chapter, we review video frames of young athletes who run fast to demonstrate that the correct technique is natural. We analyze what they are doing correctly and what they need to improve. From there we share suggestions to help coaches provide effective direction and produce consistent results. We cover principles of communication and motor learning. We finish the chapter with some additional coaching suggestions to help coaches plan out their programs.

The Correct Technique is Natural

Let's examine video frames of a few young athletes who run fast **(Fig.58-60)**. These kids were aged 6-9 at the time of filming. While their technique is not perfect, they generally have:

- good body position throughout their stride
- a complete arm stroke
- a fully extending hip on takeoff
- correct foot placement

We have made notations on each athlete to indicate what they are doing correctly and what needs improvement. It may be helpful to refer back to the details in Chapter 2 during review.

Athlete – 6 years old

CORRECT

- Pelvis is upright and head and torso are aligned (2,4).
- Opening elbow on the downstroke (1, 3).
- Full extension of hips at takeoff on both sides (2,4).

- Neutral ankle and foot placement throughout the run (2,3).

NEEDS IMPROVEMENT

- Watch for trunk flexing on landing (1,3).
- Shoulders should remain parallel in the direction of the run (1). Rather than twisting the shoulders from right to left, he needs to swing the arms *through their full range of motion from the shoulder.*
- The hand should stop at shoulder level in the front (4), and the elbow should reach 90 degrees in the back (2).

Athlete – 7 years old

2

1

4

3

CORRECT

- Head and torso are aligned throughout the run.
- Neutral ankle and foot placement under COM throughout the run (1,3).
- Shoulders are parallel (1,3,4).
- Correct downstroke (1) opens to backstroke (2).
- Correct arm stroke ends with 90-degree elbow in the back and lead hand at shoulder height (4).
- Full extension of hips at takeoff on both sides (2, 4).

NEEDS IMPROVEMENT

- Watch for shoulder twist left to right (2), which will prevent range of motion from the shoulders. Arms should swing from the shoulders.

- More consistency on arm stroke. The final arm movement should show the lead hand at shoulder height and the back elbow at a 90-degree angle (4). This is the end result of the correct arm stroke.

Athlete – 9 years old

CORRECT

- Head and torso are aligned throughout the run.
- Neutral ankle (2,4) and foot placement is under COM.
- Shank is perpendicular to the ground on landing (1, 3).
- Correct downstroke (1) opens to complete backstroke (2). Correct arm stroke ends with 90-degree elbow in the back and lead hand at shoulder height.
- Full extension of hips at takeoff on both sides (2, 4).

NEEDS IMPROVEMENT

- Watch for shoulder twist left to right (4), which will prevent range of motion from the shoulders. Arms should swing from the shoulders.

Athlete – 9 years old

2

1

4

3

CORRECT

- Pelvis is upright and head and torso are aligned (2,4).
- Opens elbow on downstroke (1) and has good backstroke (2).
- Shoulders are parallel and in the direction of the run and arms stroke from the shoulders with complete range of motion (4).
- Full extension of both hips at takeoff.
- Foot placement under COM.

NEEDS IMPROVEMENT

- Watch for body twisting (1).
- Keep the ankle neutral.
- Watch for over emphasis on arm stroke (4). Hands should reach shoulder level in the front and a 90-degree elbow in the back.

By observing young athletes, we get a glimpse of how people naturally run and the process of motor development that occurs in all of us. While their technique is not perfect, these young athletes demonstrate *that the correct way to run fast is natural.*

Unfortunately, sometimes incorrect coaching unravels our natural inclination. For athletes who have been competing since childhood, it is possible they have developed a number *of incorrect habits that will inhibit their optimum speed.*

Changing habits can be difficult, especially if what the athlete has been doing has been "good enough so far" to be successful. Success at a young age often allows flaws to persist that will hinder later development. Changing habits takes time, effort and focus. Here we offer some ideas that may help.

Communicate for Their Learning

As athletes sprint or run, it's important to communicate how to develop the correct movement patterns in a way they will understand and learn. Every athlete can learn in multiple ways but they prefer to learn in specific ways – watching demonstrations of technique or imagining how it should look, listening for cues or verbal descriptions, or physically performing the skill. All three styles are useful at various times, but athletes will rely on one style more than the others when learning a skill for the first time or trying to correct a previously acquired skill. The coach has the opportunity to help the athlete discover their preference, then balance that with what's appropriate and available during practice.

COACHES NOTE

Each coach will have a unique vocabulary. Use the same words frequently and consistently to help messages become ingrained in the training system.

The Points of Focus for Consistent Communication

Here are several **Points of Focus** that Coach Tellez developed. These cues use visually descriptive words so that the coach can demonstrate and connect with the athlete's imagination. They can be used as verbal cues during practice and during competition:

1. Upright body position, no tension
2. Stroke the arms correctly
3. Put the foot down
4. Project yourself into the next stride

Upright Body Position, No Tension

1. The torso is directly over the hips, face and shoulders are relaxed, and the head is in natural alignment.
2. The shoulders and hips are parallel in the direction of the run.
3. The feet land directly under the athlete's COM and are there for support.
4. The athlete's COM undulates with each stride; it does not stay flat.
5. The action of the quadriceps and calf muscles is automatic and is naturally coordinated with extension of the hip at take-off.
6. Upright body position enables optimal hip rotation, stride frequency, takeoff velocity and stride length.

Stroke the Arms Correctly

1. **The arms control the range of motion and tempo in the stride.**
2. The arms control the action of the legs and contribute to the total force being applied against the ground.
3. The downward stroke involves lengthening the pendulum. As the elbow goes back to 90 degrees, there will be a "catch" at the shoulder that will bring the arm forward faster in a more flexed position.
4. The distance runner's arm stroke has a shorter (quieter) range of motion.
5. The distance runner's pendulum length changes are lessened.
6. The hand and wrist function as extensions of the pendulum. Keep the wrist straight and aligned with the forearm.
7. Speed of the arm stroke must increase to increase speed.
8. As speed increases, the arms must also move through their full and correct range of motion.

Put the Foot Down

1. The ankle is held in a neutral position as the foot makes contact with the ground; it is not dorsi-or plantar-flexed.
2. The function of the foot is to support the body.
3. Place the foot under the COM.
   A. Foot contact is made low on the ball of the foot (sprinters).
   B. Foot contact is mid-foot or whole-foot (distance runners).
4. When the foot makes contact with the ground, make no effort to move the foot.
   A. The heel will naturally touch the ground so there is no need to focus on this aspect of touch-down mechanics.
   B. Force-enhancing mechanisms at the ankle and calf will facilitate the leg swing, and the foot will naturally leave the ground.
5. The foot must stop momentarily to apply force and support the body.

Project Yourself Into the Next Stride

1. The leg muscles deliver force to the ground through the foot.
2. Exploit the force-enhancing mechanisms in the hip (the pre-stretch and stretch reflex) that help generate higher angular velocity that facilitates rapid leg swing.
3. The action of the hip extensors directs the entire leg down and back for correct application of force.
4. Hip rotation is crucial for increasing and maintaining speed.
5. Focus on projecting the body into the next stride.
6. DO NOT REACH with the landing leg
   A. Reaching decreases hip rotation, produces greater braking forces and increases demand on the hamstring, which may lead to injury.
7. Keep the ankle neutral and the leg shank perpendicular to the ground for a correct landing.

COACHES NOTE

It's vital that the verbal cue connects with what the athlete feels and experiences. The athlete needs to understand what it means and feels like to "put the foot down" before the cue is given. The cue needs to lead to the correct action. If it doesn't, it's a sign that the athlete is not connecting with the phrase being used.

Emphasize Correct Technique at All Times

Whether the athlete is developing a new skill or correcting one that is inhibiting performance, structural changes in the brain and functional changes in the nervous system are what build reliability and consistency. These neuromuscular patterns are the signals between the nervous system and the body's muscles and tendons that cause joints to move in certain ways. They elicit specific actions and reactions to create movement and motor skills.

Neuromuscular patterns develop over time and through repetition and will elicit either correct OR incorrect technique. Therefore, if the athlete has been taught and/or has practiced incorrect skills, they will have learned these incorrect behaviors just as well as they will learn correct ones.

The challenge for the coach is to filter out what needs to be left alone and focus on what needs to be changed. From there, emphasis on correct execution is imperative. Assuming the athlete has the physical fitness to perform the skill correctly, they must practice until they do so, then continue to *practice until they perform the skill correctly AND consistently.*

Drills to Develop the Fundamentals of the Correct Technique

Many skills can be broken down into drills that develop individual elements by *teaching how they feel* when executed correctly. Simple drills will help the athlete develop the correct neuromuscular patterns that can then be combined to execute the correct skill.

Here are examples of effective drills that can be accomplished as a progression. To maximize their value, film the athlete from the dominant side and review the film together.

Drill 1 - Teach the Feel of Correct Application of Force Against the Ground

1. While standing still, place the hands on the hips and confirm placement on the hip flexors and extensors **(Fig. 61)**.

POSITION OF HANDS ON HIPS

Figure 61 - Fingers are spread around the hips. In the front, the index fingers point toward each other, just below the navel. In the back, the thumbs rest atop the buttocks.

2. With an upright body position, begin to walk. Feel the tension shift from the hip flexors to the extensors as the COM passes over the foot **(Fig. 62)**.

WALK WITH HANDS ON HIPS

Figure 62 – Walking slowly helps the athlete feel the stretch in the hip flexors through the fingers. The thumbs in the back will help the athlete feel the tension shift from the hip flexors to the hip extensors as the COM passes over the foot. There should be a slight flexion in the knee joint.

The athlete should walk with a heel-ball action and roll over the big toe. This will only be the case when they are walking. The lower leg will appear forward when walking. The COM will slightly undulate.

3. Moving to a slow jog, the athlete should continue to feel the stretch of the hip flexors as they land and apply force to the ground with the leg **(Fig. 63)**. This application of force is what will push the body forward and upward.

JOG WITH HANDS ON HIPS, GRADUALLY INCREASE SPEED

| 1 | 2 | 3 | 4 | 5 | 6 |

Figure 63 – As the athlete jogs, confirm that they still feel the stretch of the hip flexors and extensors as they correctly apply force to the ground. Pressing downward and slightly backward will propelthe body forward and slightly upward. Notice the COM undulation.

COACHES NOTE

As the athlete increases speed, the hip extension will become more complete and they will begin to feel the action of the stretch reflex mechanisms that increase the angular velocity of the trailing leg to naturally bring it through. There is no lifting of the knee.

Once they move to a jog and then to a sprint, the ground contact should be at mid-foot. They should maintain a neutral ankle joint and always land under the COM, with the lower leg perpendicular to the ground **(Fig. 63, frames 3 and 6)**.

Once the athlete is consistently and correctly applying force to the ground, confirm the athlete has developed the correct arm stroke using the next drill.

Drill 2 - Practice the Arm Stroke While Standing Still

The arms control range of motion and tempo in the stride. Pendulum length changes increase application of force on the opposite side and stretch reflex and force enhancement mechanisms naturally return the arm to the correct starting position. Consistent execution of this process is required for maximum speed.

ARM STROKE

Figure 64 – Sprinter's arm stroke. Confirm pendulum length changes, stopping points in the back and front, the 90 degree elbow in the back and wrist-to-hand alignment. Make sure the upper arm doesn't go beyond parallel to the ground. Keep an eye out for arms' cross-over in the front.

1. Start slowly. Sprinters should complete the pendulum length changes on the downstroke, feel the range of motion and the "catch" at the shoulder on the backstroke that initiates the stretch reflex and force enhancement mechanisms. The elbow should reach 90 degrees in the back, with the forearm directed to the ground **(Fig. 64, frames 3 and 4)**. The upstroke will naturally take a shorter path and should end with the hand just forward of the chin **(Fig. 64, frames 5 and 6)**.

2. Distance runners will perform fewer changes in pendulum length and go through a smaller range of motion. Their arm stroke will not open significantly on the back swing (review **Fig. 53**). However, competitive distance runners will use the sprinter's arm stroke when they enter the final stretch of their race.

3. Always keep the torso facing the direction of the run (no twisting), and swing from the shoulders, independent from the trunk. Minimize tension in the arms.

4. Increase speed of the arm stroke and confirm that the complete arm stroke is being performed correctly.

Drill 3 - Combine the Correct Application of Force with the Correct Arm Stroke

Once the athlete is consistently executing the drills above, put them together and increase speed from a jog to a sprint **(Fig. 65)**. This will demonstrate how the correct arm stroke

JOGGING

SPRINTING

Figure 65 – The correct arm stroke, combined with the correct application of force against the ground, optimizes stride length and maximizes speed.

BE SURE THE ATHLETE MAINTAINS CORRECT BODY POSIITON.

controls range of motion and tempo in the stride and how pendulum length changes increase the force applied against the ground on the opposite side. Note that the arm stroke will increase speed as the athlete gets faster.

This combination of the correct mechanics builds momentum, naturally increases stride length, stride frequency and ultimately maximizes SPEED.

Be Patient as Skills Develop

New skills or changes to existing ones will take time to develop. The amount of time will depend on the difficulty of the skill being acquired, the coach's vocabulary, the athlete's ability to learn it as well as their motivation to accomplish it. While many different performance improvement curves are possible, *the most common one would show a substantial improvement at first, followed by more gradual improvement as practice continues, until the athlete performs the skill correctly consistently* **(Fig. 66)**.

In all cases, performance improvement will reach what's called a "ceiling", meaning no more meaningful improvement should be expected from additional practice.

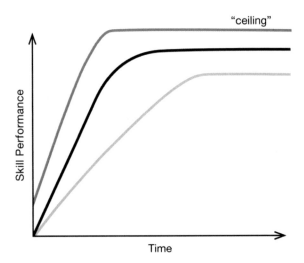

Figure 66 – Each athlete will begin with a different skill level, improve at a different rate and reach a unique "ceiling" of ability to perform a skill correctly.

COACHES NOTE

For the athlete to maintain a performance level, they must continue to perform the skill. If the athlete stops practicing, it's likely their performance will regress temporarily. However, a well-honed pattern will return quickly.

A detailed examination of the athlete's performance improvement curve will likely reveal some variability. The reason for this is that the athlete must think about the (new) skill and make the conscious choice to execute it differently than before. As practice continues, performance will become less variable and more consistent **(Fig. 67)**. As the new or corrected skills accumulate into automatic movement patterns, results should become more consistent. Changes will show in faster times and/or a feeling of less effort required to get the job done.

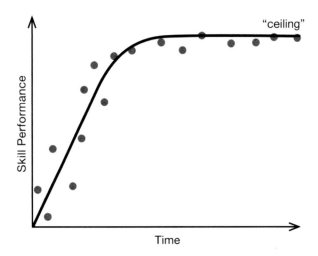

Figure 67 - Performance will become more consistent over time.

COACHES NOTE

A change in one pattern may affect other aspects that were working fine in the first place. The athlete must learn to incorporate the new motor pattern into their system.

Continue to cue the same Points of Focus during practice and before every competition, using the cues that emphasize what's correct. Help the athlete internalize the vocabulary as an additional pattern. If the athlete continues to struggle, go back to the communication and change the vocabulary, making sure the words connect to the feeling and action. Find a way to connect with the athlete to obtain the correct result.

Additional Training and Coaching Suggestions

1. Sprinters need to run fast to learn how to run fast. While we don't focus on specific workouts in this book, *there's no need to overdo it.* Train smarter, not harder. Focus on quality and always insist on correct technique

2. Training routines and sessions should be tailored to the individual athlete. Even when training in a group, give each athlete a target intensity to train at, something that stresses them without injury. Always be prepared to change the plan—harder or easier—depending on how the athlete is doing on the day. Watch for signs of fatigue and observe how quickly athletes are recovering.

3. While stride frequency and stride length are the two kinematic variables that define speed, we believe that they are the intended consequences of correct technique. *Efficient use of the body's lever systems and the correct application of force are the elements to coach.*

4. Consider breaking practices up into technical skills days vs. running days.

   A. Practice block settings and starts on technical days. Block settings and SET position practice sessions can also happen in groups. Use photography and/or a clipboard to document personal details for each athlete.

   B. Sprinters need to run fast to learn how to run fast. Use short sprint breakdowns, e.g., a 400/300/200 in pre-season, then a 300/200/100 in season. Ask athletes to run at maximum speed and record their times. Mid-week tempo runs like Repeat 200s / Repeat 150s that drop time and recovery windows as the season progresses will develop speed AND anaerobic endurance. Coaches, *there's no need to overdo it.* And, as we've said before, ALWAYS insist on correct technique on running days.

   C. On running days, workouts on gradual hills help athletes learn how to run upright, apply force to the ground and stroke the arms correctly to get up the hill. Hills work should carry over to the flat track.

5. Whereas the short distance sprinter primarily relies on the use of anaerobic pathways to produce energy, the distance athlete primarily uses oxygen. To improve performance, distance athletes must increase their aerobic capacity. The way to do this is with long runs.

   Train distance runners based on running time. Workouts expand to last between 1-1/2 to 2 hours to build endurance in the muscles.

6. Coach the causes and effects. Every mechanical action has a consequence. Observe, link to the cause, then coach the change.

7. In addition to using verbally descriptive cues as they practice, provide immediate feedback and validate progress through video review. Slow motion video helps the coach and athlete assess what the athlete is doing correctly or needs to improve.

COACHES NOTE

Video can be captured by other athletes during practice. Use a smartphone or tablet on a video setting that maximizes the frames per second. Slow motion is ideal. For best results shoot the video from the athlete's dominant side. Definitely shoot from the same side in practice that you would shoot in a meet so you can compare the two.

8. As with the discussion of how consistent execution of technical skills will serve to change the underlying neuromuscular patterns, consistent and repetitive activities will also calm the athlete's mind. Examples include using the same warm-up routine at every practice and (an extended version of the same) before every competition. Add a walking lap or two to help athletes clear their head and become aware of their environment. Always review the Points of Focus and insist on correct execution.

9. Confidence is important. Confidence comes from executing consistently and accomplishing a plan. *Teach athletes what to do, so when they go to competition all they have to do is execute.* Create the training plan so expectations are clear. Include (easier) competitions that will build their confidence. Above all, be consistent and communicate in a way that will help them stay motivated.

10. As athletes mature, focus on the performance, not the place. Awards and trophies are helpful to motivate younger athletes to learn and improve. However, as they work harder and refine their skills because they enjoy the sport and really want to perform their very best, their reason for learning becomes internal. Help them stay motivated by focusing on their personal progress.

11. Use training drills that develop the correct technique. Be careful of the ones that don't.

Here are three examples of drills to examine:

A. <u>Staying Low Out of the Blocks.</u> Block clearance sets up the athlete's acceleration pattern and body position. As shown in **Figure 68**, a lower body angle coming out of the blocks may seem to create more forward progress, but the athlete's steps will actually be quicker and shorter. Quicker steps limit the amount of force that can be applied to the ground, inhibiting the athlete's generation of momentum at this critical phase. The body position that applies maximum horizontal and vertical force to the ground is 45 degrees. The best start utilizes a body position that is aligned from head to toe, with maximum force applied against the ground with deliberate, forceful, steps that will optimize acceleration **(Fig. 69)**.

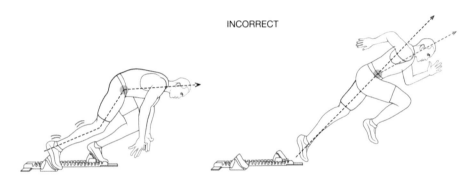

Figure 67 - An INCORRECT block start will appear low and may include a break at the waist.

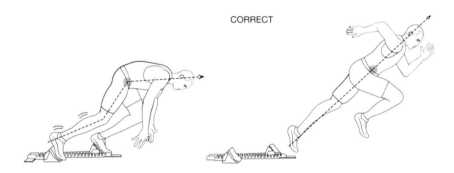

Figure 68 - The correct block start shows head and torso alignment and lets the body rise to 45 degrees. The athlete will take advantage of maximum horizontal AND vertical forces to overcome inertia and gravity and set up the optimal acceleration pattern.

B. <u>Pulling Sleds.</u> The idea behind pulling sleds is to develop additional strength to overcome inertia and horizontal force, including possibly wind resistance on competition day. While commonly used in practice, the literature is mixed on the performance benefits because *it may put correct technique at risk.*

In addition to the risk of lower back injury, there is a possibility of reduced performance due to:

1) Incorrect application of force
2) Reduced stride length
3) Reduced stride frequency
4) Increased torso lean
5) Increased ground contact
6) Inhibited hip rotation due to changes in the action of the leg's lever system

In other words, pulling a sled can potentially throw the body into the incorrect position. If the sled is too heavy or the load distribution isn't correct, the athlete cannot run correctly. Due to potential discrepancies in the athletes' training status and load distribution (height of the strap), we advise coaches to proceed with caution.

Remember, *the human body is made to push,* not pull. A more effective use of sleds would be to push them to teach the deliberate and forceful first three strides at the start that will set the body up for a smooth acceleration. *Create the "pushing the car" analogy from Chapter 2.*

C. <u>Knee Lifting Drills.</u> Drills that cause the athlete to lift the knees teach incorrect technique. To review, *the knee should rise as a result* of application of force against the ground, enhanced by the pre-stretch / stretch reflex mechanisms. Rather than focusing on lifting the knee, the athlete should enable the legs to cycle naturally by applying force to the ground downward and backward. The knee will come forward as a result.

As an example, if mini hurdles or wickets are part of the drill curriculum, we suggest performing them with the hands on the hips. A "no arms" approach minimizes the athlete's ability to lift the knees, and causes them to apply force to the ground instead. Other examples of effective drills would be skipping, fast marching, plyometric box jumps or bounding. All of these drills develop the legs and maintain the integrity of applying force to the ground in the correct direction.

12. Relax and remember, *not every athlete will be fast, but every athlete can get faster. Set the tone for a training journey that focuses on that goal.*

Summary

Previous chapters presented the science of speed, the fundamental principles, why they matter and how to apply them as elements of running and sprinting technique. In this chapter, we focused on how to teach them in ways that will deliver consistent performance and optimal results. Our objective is to complement the science with some professional wisdom and recommendations that will make the coach's job easier and their athletes more successful.

Reliable, consistent performance of the correct technique is the ultimate objective. Similar to the scientific principles of motion, the principles of motor learning are proven and repeatable. Athletes will learn differently and at different rates. Communicate in ways that reach the athlete. Use consistent verbal descriptions, visual aids and always insist on correct technique. Athletes may get worse before they get better because they are practicing, but performance will improve as they practice.

Appendix A

Vocabulary

Newton's First Law: An object continues in a state of rest, or in a state of motion at a constant velocity along a straight line, unless compelled to change that state by a net force.

Newton's Second Law: Relating force, Mass and Acceleration, force equals mass times acceleration.

Newton's Third Law: Whenever one body exerts a force on a second body, the second body also exerts an equal and opposite force back on the first body.
• •

Δ: Symbol that indicates difference or "change" in the variable that follows it

acceleration: The rate of change of *velocity*, expressed as a vector

angular acceleration: The rate of change of *angular velocity*

angular displacement: The angle between the initial and final angular positions

angular momentum: The product of an object's *moment of inertia* and its *angular velocity*

angular velocity: The rate of change of *angular displacement*

axis: A straight line about which a body rotates

center of mass (gravity): The location where the force of gravity acts on the body, taken as the point where the mass of the entire body is concentrated. in a body where force acts

centripetal acceleration: The *acceleration* needed to keep an object in circular motion; centripetal acceleration is directed toward the center of the circle

centripetal force: The *force;* directed toward the center of the circle, that keeps an object going in circular motion

conservation of energy: The law of physics that says that the total energy of a closed system doesn't change

displacement: The change in an object's position in terms of distance and direction

energy: The ability of a system to do *work*

frequency: The number of cycles of a periodic behavior per unit of time

friction: The force between two surfaces that always acts to oppose any relative movement between them

gravity: The force which causes objects to move vertically downward toward the center of the earth.

impulse: The product of the amount of force on an object and the time during which the force is applied

inertia: The tendency of a mass to resist a change in motion

kilogram: The *MKS* unit of *mass*

kinematics: The branch of *mechanics* concerned with motion without reference to *force* or *mass*

kinetic energy: The *energy* of an object due to its motion

kinetic friction: *Friction* that resists the motion of an object that's already moving

law of conservation of momentum: A law stating that the momentum of a system doesn't change unless influenced by an external force

lever: a rigid bar which pivots on a fulcrum

linear motion: Straight-line movement from one point to another

linear momentum: The product of an object's mass times its velocity; momentum is a vector

magnitude: The size, amount, or length associated with a scalar or vector quantity (scalars are defined by magnitude only, while vectors are defined by magnitude and direction)

mass: The quantitative measure of the property that makes matter resist acceleration

mechanics: The area of physics that deals with the motions of bodies and the forces imposed upon them

MKS system: The measurement system that uses meters, kilograms, and seconds

momentum: The product of mass times velocity

moment of inertia: The property of matter that makes it resist rotational acceleration

moment arm of a force: The perpendicular distance from the axis of rotation to the line of action of a force

oscillate: Move from side to side or swing back and forth in a regular fashion

period: The time it takes for one complete cycle of a repeating event

potential energy: The energy an object has because of its internal configuration or its position when a force is acting on it

power: The rate at which work is done by a system

scalar: A mathematical construct that has magnitude but not direction (in contrast to a vector, which has both)

specific gravity: The density of a substance relative to a reference substance

static friction: Friction on a stationary object

torque: The product of a force and the force's perpendicular distance to that turning point

translatory motion: occurs when all points in the body move the same distance in the same amount of time but may not be moving in a straight line

vector: A mathematical construct that has both a magnitude and a direction

velocity: The time rate of change of an object's position, expressed as a vector whose magnitude is speed

weight: The force exerted on a mass by a gravitational field

work: Force multiplied by the displacement over which that force acts and the cosine of the angle between them; force is equal to the amount of energy transferred by a force

Appendix B

The Mechanical Elements of Speed

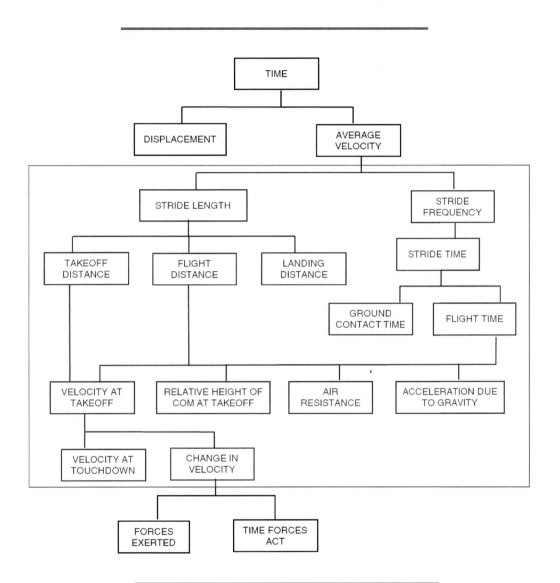

These elements are Influenced by body position and arm stroke.

Appendices and References

Appendix C

Correct Running Mechanics in Action

This 13-year-old athlete demonstrates the elements of Body Position, Arm Stroke and Stride Cycle detailed in Chapter 2 (**Fig. 69 and 70**). When performed correctly as independent actions, these elements create an *interdependent system* for optimal speed. Note that the dominant side will generally operate slightly differently – and more correctly - than the non-dominant side.

Figure 69 – The correct mechanics optimize vertical and horizontal forces.

Figure 70 – The correct mechanics optimize stride length and tempo for speed.

BODY POSITION – Determines How Far the Body Will Travel with Each Stride

- Pelvis is upright and head and torso are aligned above the pelvis
- Foot lands below the COM (no "reaching")
- Upright position enables full extension of the hip at takeoff in order to maximize available vertical and horizontal forces in the correct direction
- Hips that extend fully through their full range of motion also activates the stretch reflex at the hip that allows the trailing leg to swing through naturally with maximum angular velocity (no "lifting")
- Shoulders are relaxed and parallel in the direction of the run

ARM STROKE – Controls Range of Motion in the Stride and Tempo

- Elbow extends on the downstroke to increase its pendulum length, which increases force applied to the ground on the opposite side
- 90-degree elbow on the backstroke activates the stretch reflex mechanism at the shoulder to return the arm forward with maximum angular velocity
- Elbow flexes on the upstroke to decrease its pendulum length and stops at shoulder level to prepare for the next downstroke
- Hands and wrists are aligned to operate as extensions of the arm lever system
- Shoulders are relaxed, parallel in the direction of the run, with no twisting
- Consistent arm stroke on both sides

STRIDE CYCLE – The Correct Application of Force Maximizes Stride Length

- Foot/ankle position remains neutral throughout the stride
- Mid-foot landing ("Just put the foot down.")
- The landing shank is perpendicular to the ground and the foot lands under the COM, minimizing landing distance (absolutely no "reaching")
- The application of force against the ground is down and back, overcoming gravity and causing full extension of the hip, which activates the stretch reflex mechanisms in the hip and leg to increase the angular velocity of the leg as it automatically cycles through (no "lifting or butt kicking"). The greater the force against the ground, the more angular velocity of the leg, and this combination is what optimizes range of motion in the stride and tempo.
- Consistent stride cycle on both sides.

Appendix D

Sprinter's Start Mechanics in Action

The same 13-year-old athlete demonstrates the sprinter's block start. As we have discussed, the correct block settings and block clearance mechanics are crucial to executing a start that will maximize speed. Getting to the right block settings takes some practice and repetition from the SET position. Adjustments may need to be made to assure optimum positioning.

"Runners, Take Your Marks"

- Strong leg is forward in the blocks, with the shank of the lower leg parallel to the ground and the knee even with the forearm
- Toes of the front foot rest on the track
- Rear knee is on the ground and adjacent to the front toe. Leg length may affect this slightly by 3-5 inches
- Tip of the toes of the rear foot are on the track.
- Hands are bridged on the ground, directly below the shoulders, with the arms fully extended
- Weight of the body appears balanced between the hands and the rear knee
- Head and neck are in alignment with the spine and the eyes are looking downward
- Appears relaxed

Figure 71 – "Take Your Marks"

Transitioning to the Optimal SET Position

Figure 72 – The optimal SET position prepares for a successful block clearance.

- Hips rise so knee angles are 90 degrees (front) and 130-135 degrees (rear)
- Both ankles appear to be close to neutral
- Head and torso are in natural alignment
- Degree of forward lean is minimal, just slightly forward
- Eyes are now focused between the athlete's hands and front foot
- Application of force against both blocks appears balanced

SET   TAKE YOUR MARKS

Figure 73 – Detail of foot placement and transition from MARKS to SET.

- Front foot is initially positioned at TAKE YOUR MARKS so that the toes are resting on the track and the foot is relaxed. On transition to the SET position, the ankle joint opens to allow the foot to rest against the block.
- Rear foot is placed at TAKE YOUR MARKS so the tip of the big toe is just touching the track. Rising to the SET position, the heel moves back while the lower part of the foot maintains pressure against the block. Depending on the block type, the foot could make more contact than shown here.

Reaction Time and Block Clearance

Figure 73 – A successful block clearance to a 45-degree angle of projection.

- Full hip extension to approach a 45-degree angle of projection
    - Needs to correct head position to maintain alignment with torso
- Arm opposite the front knee extends straight and upward to allow more time to apply force to the front block
- Front arm is flexed and mirrors the angle of the knee on the opposite leg
- Front shin appears to be at 45 degrees from the ground, with a neutral ankle prepared for landing

COACHES NOTE

When resistance is at its highest, it takes longer to go through the stride cycle, so stride frequency is going to be low at the start. Strides will also be the shortest.

Always focus on the correct mechanics, not quickness, as the athlete clears the blocks. Consistent, correct application of force will cause stride frequency - and stride length- to naturally increase for a smooth and efficient acceleration.

**Figure 74 – The correct start maximizes velocity out of the blocks
and enables a smooth acceleration.**

- First stride is the shortest, and every step is forceful and deliberate
- Lands on the ball of the foot with the COM directly over the foot
- Ankle joint of the landing leg remains neutral
- Full extension of the hip on every takeoff maximizes application of force on the ground
- Application of force transfers to "down and slightly back"
- Maintains consistent head-to-torso alignment throughout
- Body gradually rises on each stride to obtain the upright position required for efficient acceleration
- Elbows and arms stay close to the body (medially)
- Elbow opens on the downstroke to maximize force applied to the ground on the opposite leg
- Elbow closes in the back to complete the arm stroke and initiate a stretch reflex in the shoulder, which causes the elbow to close and the arm to swing forward
- *Arm action matches the opposite leg action in force and range of motion*

References

1. Kenney, W. L., Wilmore J. H. & Costill, D. (2015). *Physiology of Sport and Exercise (6th ed.).* Illinois, IL: Human Kinetics.

2. Counsilman, J. E. (1968). *The Science of Swimming.* New Jersey, NJ: Prentice-Hall.

3. Dyson, G. H. G. (1962). *The Mechanics of Athletics.* London, LDN: University of London Press

4. Ecker, T. (1985). *Basic Track & Field Biomechanics.* California, CA: Tafnews Press

5. Harewood, Dave. Sprinting - A Biomechanical Analysis. (unpublished)

6. Hamill, J., Knutzen, K. & Derrick, T. (2014). *Biomechanical Basis of Human Movement (4th ed.).* Pennsylvania, PA: Lippincott Williams & Wilkins.

7. Hay, J. G. (1993). *The Biomechanics of Sports Techniques (4th ed.).* New Jersey, NJ: Prentice-Hall.

8. McArdle W.A, Katch, F.I. and Katch, V.L. (2014) *Exercise Physiology: Nutrition, Energy, and Human Performance.* Wolters Kluwer Health/Lippincott Williams & Williams.

9. Novachek, T. F. (1998). The Biomechanics of Running. *Gait & Posture, 7(1),* 77-95.

10. Vaughan, C. L. (1984). Biomechanics of Running Gait. *Journal of Critical Reviews in biomedical Engineering, 12(1),* 1-48.

11. Weyand, P. G., Sternlight, D. B., Bellizzi, M. J., & Wright, S. (2000). Faster top running speeds are achieved with greater ground forces not more rapid leg movements. *Journal of Applied Physiology, 85(5),* 1991-2000.

12. Winter, D. A. (2009). *Biomechanics and Motor Control of Human Movement (4TH ed.)*. New York, NY: John Wiley & Sons.

13. Wilt, F. (1967, September). Track Technique. *Track and Field News, 29*, 898-928.

14. Petrakos, G., Morin, J. B., & Egan, B. (2016). Resisted Sled Sprint Training to Improve Sprint Performance: A Systematic Review. *Journal of Sports Medicine, 46(3)*, 381-400. doi: 10.1007/s40279-015-0422-8.

15. Argubi-Wollesen, A., Wollesen, B., Leitner M., and Mattes, K. (2017). Human Body Mechanics of Pushing and Pulling: Analyzing the Factors of Task-related Strain on the Musculoskeletal System. *Safety and Health at Work, 8(1)*, 11-18. doi: 10.1016/j.shaw.2016.07.003

16. Young, H. D. (1992). *University Physics (8th ed.)*. Reading, Mass: Addison-Wesley Publishing Company.

17. Enoka, R. M. (2001). *Neuromechanics of Human Movement (3rd ed.)*. Illinois, IL: Human Kinetics.

18. Rose, D. J. & Christina, R W. (2005). *A Multilevel Approach to the Study of Motor Control and Learning (2nd ed.)*. London, LDN: Pearson.

19. Schmidt, R. & Lee, T. (2011). *Motor Control and Learning: A Behavioural Emphasis (5th ed.)*. Illinois, IL: Human Kinetics.

Made in the USA
Coppell, TX
24 April 2021